THE THERAPEUTIC DIALOGUE

A Method for the Analysis of Verbal Interaction

THE THERAPEUTIC DIALOGUE

A Method for the Analysis of Verbal Interaction

By

JEROME L. SCHULMAN, M.D.

Associate Professor of Pediatrics
Associate Professor of Psychiatry and Neurology
Northwestern University Medical School
Attending Psychiatrist
Children's Memorial Hospital
Chicago, Illinois

JOSEPH C. KASPAR, Ph.D.

Associate in Pediatrics (Psychology)
Northwestern University Medical School
Chief Psychologist
Children's Memorial Hospital
Chicago, Illinois
Lecturer in Child Clinical Psychology
Northwestern University
Evanston, Illinois

PATRICIA M. BARGER, Ph.D.

Instructor in Pediatrics (Psychology)
Northwestern University Medical School
Staff Psychologist
Children's Memorial Hospital
Chicago, Illinois

CHARLES C THOMAS • PUBLISHER
Springfield • Illinois • U.S.A.

Published and Distributed Throughout the World by
CHARLES C THOMAS • PUBLISHER
BANNERSTONE HOUSE
301-327 East Lawrence Avenue, Springfield, Illinois, U.S.A.
NATCHEZ PLANTATION HOUSE
735 North Atlantic Boulevard, Fort Lauderdale, Florida, U.S.A.

Library of Congress Catalog Card Number: 64-16101

Printed in the United States of America
W-2

ACKNOWLEDGMENTS

As ONE reconstructs the process involved in preparing a book of this kind one is struck with the number of debts one has accrued, intellectually and emotionally.

The core of the book, those chapters dealing with the analysis of verbal productions, had its beginnings in a series of meetings held for psychiatric residents by Dr. Eugene Meyer, which were attended by the senior author.

This debt is further extended to all of our teachers, therapy supervisors, colleagues and students who have contributed immeasurably to the ideas and content of the book.

A more specific debt of gratitude is owed to a number of persons who took time out from their own busy schedules to read the volume, and were kind enough to make specific criticisms. This source of information was invaluable in adding precision and clarification to the book. These persons are: Heinz L. Ansbacher, Bernard M. Aronov, Bion Barger, Barbara Burmeister, Allan F. Demorest, Jerome D. Frank, Kenneth Howard, George G. Katz, Jack Kysar, Robert B. Lawson, William S. Littlewood, Nancy Orlinsky, Lenore Schulman, Fred E. Spaner, Janet Taylor Spence, Jack J. Teplinsky, Eberhard Uhlenhuth, and David T. A. Vernon.

The authors would like to express their appreciation to their families and to Children's Memorial Hospital for providing a setting of encouragement and interest without which the book could not have been written.

We are grateful to the Field Foundation whose generous support has provided stimulation for this and other work.

Finally, we owe an immeasurable debt of gratitude to Mrs. Edith Baker Lichterman who has typed and read and mimeographed and proof read and typed and typed and typed.

Ultimately, however, this book is dedicated to those to whom we owe our greatest debt; our patients.

J. L. S.
J. C. K.
P. M. B.

Contents

THE THERAPEUTIC DIALOGUE

A Method for the Analysis of Verbal Interaction

Chapter I

INTRODUCTION

THIS BOOK IS the result of the authors' experiences in learning, practicing and teaching psychotherapy. Interpersonal relations are complex and difficult to understand at best. The problems are magnified when, as in psychotherapy, one attempts to study the distortions existing in a relationship while simultaneously participating in its evolution. Our effort here is to set forth a series of techniques which may assist the therapist in studying the patient's verbal productions and his own. These are presented in a fashion which can provide a framework for the supervision of therapy. It is our hope that these techniques may prove particularly useful to the new therapist who may feel uncomfortable with his initial attempts to deal therapeutically with others. As experience and facility with psychotherapeutic techniques improve, this approach should become progressively less necessary.

It is important to realize that this volume is not intended to be a complete approach to psychotherapy. We are limiting our discussion to those techniques which we propose as a basis for approaching psychotherapy. We strongly endorse the notion that good psychotherapy is more than the sum total of techniques employed in much the same sense that a painting is more than composition, drawing and color. Just as the graphic artist must master the tools of his trade through prolonged conscientious effort, the therapist must practice and perfect his therapeutic skills before he can expect to accomplish successful therapeutic endeavors. Once there is mastery of these skills it is possible to participate in a helping relationship which is the application and blending of many composite parts into a unified process. We view psychotherapy as having a flow and character which transcends its components. However, we believe that one may look upon it as an art, the component skills of which must necessarily be acquired before a true unity can occur.

Most beginning therapists have acquired a good deal of sophistication in their understanding of dynamics and personality theory. It has seemed to us that the crucial lack in the education of the average psychotherapist occurs at the level of translating this understanding into therapeutic behaviors. Experiences with a series of beginning therapists led us to the inescapable conclusion that a serious problem existed at the level of understanding specific patient-therapist communications and that this difficulty tended to preclude the development of the art of therapy. The theoretical understanding was sterile for lack of skill in application. Having reached this conclusion, we decided to attempt to evolve a technique for supervising the beginning therapist in his specific verbal interactions.

In the past it was impossible to obtain material which was suitable for supervision at this level. Reports from notes or memories are so incomplete and may contain so much distortion as to render them of little value for this purpose. The current ease of making tape recordings provides one obvious solution to the problem of obtaining adequate reporting of the therapy session. However, there is still the problem that really adequate supervision of one therapy hour, including discussion of dynamic problems, goals, patient-therapist relationships and specific verbal exchanges almost always requires several hours. It is, therefore, a practical impossibility to provide sufficient supervisory time adequately to review a major portion of a trainee's therapeutic efforts.

In view of these considerations we have constructed a flexible system whereby the beginning therapist is able systematically to evaluate his own work from a number of viewpoints. He focuses on the various meanings of each of the patient's statements and on the nature of each of his own replies, considering both the response he actually made and responses which might have been preferable. Each of the communications is considered in relation to the therapist's knowledge of his patient, the purposes of therapy and the recent course of the treatment process. We emphasize that this system is *not* intended as a substitute for supervision by an experienced therapist but rather as both a framework for and a supplement to supervision.

When we apply this system in supervision, we request that the student undertake the type of unit communication analysis of the therapeutic interview which we will describe later. The supervisor then reviews part of the analysis with him, endeavoring to point out areas which he appears to have overlooked or inadequately understood in his initial analysis. We have found that after a student has acquired some skill in the application of this type of analysis, he can use both his own study time and his supervisory sessions more fruitfully. The system has also been employed on a peer supervision basis with groups of three or four students or staff therapists meeting together for discussion of each other's interview tapes. Our experience has been that this system, conscientiously applied, frequently results in a dramatic improvement in therapeutic technique.

The price of improvement with this system is one of arduous, gruelling toil. The system requires constant reinvestigation of the dynamic formulation, frequent reexamination of the goals of treatment and many hours of attempting to understand the meaning of the patient's statements and the inadequacies of our responses. In addition to being time consuming and intellectually taxing the system has the devastating effect of frequently exposing deficiencies in the therapist's understanding, skill and personal adjustment. If there is a short and comfortable road to success in therapy this is not it. On the other hand, we have found the rewards fully equal to the costs.

While the analysis of the specific verbal interactions of therapy represents the core of our system, several preliminary and concurrent procedures also assume substantial importance. Our plan for presentation of the system in this book is as follows:

an overview of the most significant components and their interrelationships provides the reader with a global look at the system; each of the principal components is elaborated in detail with accompanying case material; several topics, not directly related to the application of the system but philosophically relevant to it, are discussed; and finally, an annotated bibliography, designed for the student, provides a basis for further exploration of the literature. The clinical examples employed throughout the presentation are drawn from the treatment experiences of two patients, an adult woman and an adolescent boy. Examples are, for the most part, taken directly from case reports and tape transcriptions with license being employed only to protect the identity of the patients and to provide examples of phenomena which were absent in these particular therapeutic transactions.

Two aspects of the genesis of this book deserve mention. First, it is not original, at least in its elements. Much of what is proposed is fairly standard technique in some training settings, even if not formalized or explicit. On the other hand, so far as we are aware many of the specific schemes of classification proposed and much of the attempt to integrate the material are original. We have endeavored to make explicit some methods of studying therapy and have made first order approximations to a possible integration of the various components. A second aspect of the system outlined here is unique, we believe. This is the first attempt of which we are aware to propose a system for the study of the therapeutic relationship which is applicable to a variety of theoretical orientations. From the time of Freud, the thinking about psychotherapeutic procedures has been intimately linked with theorizing about personality. In many cases the basic theoretical assumptions of a theorist have been formalized as the core and substance of the therapeutic approach which he devised. One consequence of this has been a tendency to ritualize and reify a therapeutic approach upon the death of its innovator. Equally unfortunate has been the tendency to compel therapists who are in theoretical agreement with a system to utilize the technique and ritual of treatment promulgated by the system without regard for its suitability for the individual therapist.

While we believe that our approach to considering psychotherapy may be applicable to a variety of theoretical orientations, there is in this volume a basic bias toward an interpersonal dynamic view of personality which is present in both the text and the case material. We do not believe, however, that this bias extends into specific theoretical subdivisions of this general dynamic position. Among the forces which have contributed to the evolution of this scheme of studying psychotherapy is the variety of theoretical orientations which we encounter in our students. For this practical reason as well as for philosophical reasons, we desired to evolve a system which could apply to a variety of ways of looking at people and at therapy. We have not attempted to proselytize for a particular theory either in training or in this book. Therefore, our purpose is not that of indicating what constitutes desirable therapeutic behavior; rather, it is to propose a system which can increase the skill with which the desired treatment is conducted, recognizing that we are still at a point in our scientific history where a variety of therapeutic techniques must be considered quite acceptable. This combination of circumstances leads us to the position of largely divorcing the theoretical conceptualizations about psychodynamics from the specific therapy techniques. Therapeutic interactions can then be studied without proposing what an acceptable therapeutic statement must be.

Thus introduced we turn to the examination of the proposed system, remembering Hippocrate's summation of the difficulties of attempting to help, "Life is short, and the art is long. . . ."

Chapter II

AN OVERVIEW OF THE SYSTEM

IN SUCCEEDING chapters we will set forth the details of our approach to the learning of psychotherapy. At this point we will briefly summarize the essentials of the system as a means of providing a global context within which the details may later be organized.

There are a variety of theoretical orientations to psychotherapy which lead to different therapeutic maneuvers; the evidence is not at all clear as to whether any one of these orientations is generally successful and thus merits widespread adoption. It is possible, although not yet clearly demonstrated, that specific therapeutic orientations tend to be successful with particular types of patients and not with others. It is also possible that the differences in the personalities of therapists preclude the possibility of the same therapeutic maneuvers being equally applicable to all treatment situations. In many respects, therefore, the crucial variables of the therapeutic interaction are not now known. In the face of this, we would not presume to tell an individual therapist how he should behave and instead have attempted to evolve a system which is flexible enough to accommodate many points of view. However, the very fact that it is a system is anathema to some; to others the evident bias toward a dynamic orientation is unacceptable.

In our view, psychotherapy is a treatment process which should be planned in great detail for each patient, with considerable attention given to the manner of execution.

We believe that whatever his theoretical orientation, the task of the therapist is to understand and react to his patient in some manner which is helpful to the patient. Regardless of theoretical orientation, it would seem to be necessary that the therapist knows what he hopes to accomplish and how he is endeavoring to do this. We believe that he should be able to explain and defend his therapy on some rational basis.

Psychotherapy is often approached in a rather haphazard manner. The therapist usually begins by taking a history which he may never formally organize in writing; he establishes some idea of the dynamics, although again not in detailed fashion; and he starts treatment without either the patient or himself necessarily having clear ideas as to what is being treated or how the treatment is to proceed. The essence of the system which we propose involves procedures for making the therapeutic process planned, explicit and logical to the fullest extent possible. In no way is it intended to interfere with individuality or spontaneity during the conduct of the therapy hour; rather, the planning and detailed consideration takes place between sessions.

The system which we propose involves five procedures, each of which is applied repeatedly during a course of therapy. The first and most basic is that of examining one's attitudes toward people, toward patients in general and toward this patient in particular. The second procedure is that of evolving a dynamic formulation for the patient. The third involves the setting of goals for therapy and the specification of methods for achieving them. The fourth procedure is the analysis of statements made by the patient during the therapy hour; this takes place simultaneously with the fifth procedure, the analysis of the therapist's responses to the patient's statements.

The first procedure, the evaluation of one's own attitude toward people, is not easily accomplished. We believe that the successful therapist must have a positive attitude toward people in general and toward his patient in particular. In addition, we believe that people have a capacity for change and feel that this belief is a necessary prerequisite for becoming a psychotherapist. Further, we believe that it is necessary for the therapist to be able to experience positive relations with human beings himself. He must be able to accept himself as a worthwhile person. He must know from personal experience what is meant by "the warm glow of human contact." He must be able to comprehend the extreme discomfort a patient experiences. He must be able to be honest, both with himself and with his patient. When a therapist falls far short of these standards, we believe that his therapeutic endeavors are likely to be less than satisfactory. Therefore, difficult as it is, the beginning therapist should examine his attitudes toward himself and others, his ability to experience positive relationships and his attitude toward change; if he finds himself wanting in some respect he should consider the possibility that he might benefit from a therapeutic experience himself.

The remaining steps or procedures deal more directly with the individual patient. The second procedure, the construction of a dynamic formulation for the patient, depends upon a dynamic orientation toward the evolution of personality problems; this emphasis on dynamics is one of the theoretical biases incorporated in our system. The implication underlying the concept of a dynamic formulation is that the patient's behavior and feelings are the logical end products of the series of events which have occurred during the course of his life experiences and that an understanding of this series of events is an important step if one is to help him. There is no implication that constitutional endowment or subsequent somatic events play no role, for these are viewed as events in much the same sense as are interpersonal transactions. It does appear to us, however, that the major influences in producing a patient's difficulties usually have been his past interpersonal experiences. In constructing a dynamic formulation the therapist endeavors to reconstruct the chain of events in such a way that the end result, the patient's current feelings and behavior, appears to be logical. One analogy to the task of constructing a dynamic formulation would be to the work of the novelist. He must delineate a character who is believable and real and whose actions make sense in the light of all of the available information. Similiarly, the therapist must understand his patient well enough to perceive the logic of his behavior in the light of his life experiences.

The initial dynamic formulation should be written after only a few therapy hours, during which time the therapist will have acquired a surprisingly large body of information. Usually the therapist knows more about the patient at this point than would seem possible. The act of preparing the formulation provides an orienting point around which to organize one's thinking about the patient. Asking one's self questions about the accumulated material may lead to recollection of additional significant information and to restructuring and reorganizing one's initial perceptions of the patient. The first formulation may enhance the therapist's comprehension of his patient considerably by highlighting areas which need exploration and by unifying knowledge relevant to other areas of the patient's functioning. There will be certain aspects of the patient's personality which the therapist believes to have been conclusively demonstrated; these should be mentioned in the formulation with indications of the evidence upon which the conclusions are based. This evidence should include both historical information and material from the therapeutic relationship. It is worthwhile to explore the evolution of these aspects of personality in as much detail as possible. There will be other aspects of the personality about which the therapist's knowledge is poor and the evidence is sparse. In spite of this lack of knowledge it is useful to speculate about these areas since such speculation may lead to the clarification of questions which may need to be answered subsequently. There will be still other areas which one would presume to be important but about which there appears to be no information as yet. Delineating these areas can also be most helpful since some of them may later assume a critical importance.

The dynamic formulation should be rich in examples selected from the patient's anecdotes and his direct remarks to the therapist; these have the effect of producing a more human document, with a unique flavor and a genuine ring of authenticity. The therapist should attempt to employ only simple language in the formulation since complicated theoretical terminology often serves to obscure or gloss over inadequacies in understanding. The dynamic formulation must be written and explicit, rather than mental and vague; it should be rewritten periodically with the view toward achieving successive approximations of a full formulation for this unique individual.

The third procedure in the system which we advocate is the formulation of explicit goals for therapy. Goal formulation is frequently a difficult task, particularly for the beginner. However, we believe that the progress of therapy is likely to be more rapid and satisfactory if there are explicit goals which have been agreed upon by both the patient and the therapist. Further, we believe that it is desirable to be quite specific in stating goals, even though modification may be necessary as treatment progresses. It is common to formulate both short and long term goals.

Goals for treatment may be proposed by both the patient and the therapist. The patient enters treatment with definite goals of his own. Some of these goals may be unrealistic or may be expressions of his pathology. However, these should be among the goals that the therapist adopts until such time as the reasons for modifying or abandoning some of them become explicit. One short term goal, in such a situation would be that of discussing and clarifying the patient's goals, with the view to helping him to recognize the unrealistic aspects of his goal and to evolve more satisfactory ones. The therapist may propose goals which seem desirable to him at various points in treatment but he must obtain the patient's acceptance of such goals before he can hope for progress toward them.

Once the goals of a particular course of treatment have been specified, the therapist must formulate the therapeutic plans by which he hopes to achieve these goals. Toward what aspects of the patient's functioning will the therapy be directed? Are certain types of therapeutic maneuvers to be preferred over possible alternatives? As with other aspects of the therapeutic process, the clearer and more explicit our concepts, the better the results which we may hope to obtain. Therefore, we believe that it is quite necessary that the goals of therapy and the plans for approaching them be committed to writing and that they be periodically reviewed and revised if necessary.

The remaining procedures, the analyses of the patient's statements and of the therapist's responses, require the tape recording of therapy sessions. Movies would undoubtedly be preferable since they capture dimensions of behavior which a tape recording cannot encompass; unfortunately, studio facilities are neither practical nor available for most therapists. We stress the need for recording since no matter how complete our understanding of the dynamics or how desirably our goals and therapeutic plans are formulated the therapeutic process is expressed ultimately in the interactions, primarily verbal, which occur between the therapist and his patient. Therefore it behooves us to examine each statement made by the patient and by the therapist critically and to explore its meaning in a detalied manner. Such careful examination cannot be made during the ongoing therapy hour except, perhaps, after long experience and training.

Before discussing the analysis of statements in detail we should like to note that each therapy hour may be conceived of as having a theme, as does the total therapeutic process. Commonly the theme may be discerned in the opening statement of the hour, although it may not be apparent immediately. If the theme is not revealed in the early statements, it may gradually emerge as the hour unfolds. We feel that it is desirable to search for the theme, since it can stand as the signal post for the conduct of the therapeutic hour.

The analysis of the individual statements of the patient and the responses of the therapist will be treated in much greater detail later. Briefly, the patient's statement is defined as his natural conversational unit; that is, a statement includes all verbalizations from the point at which the patient begins talking until the point at which he pauses or the therapist interrupts him. Each of the patient's statements is assumed to be amenable to analysis from each of four vantage points: the content, the accompanying affect, the dynamic implications and the transference message. At first glance, the four analyses might appear to be impossible, for certain statements will appear to lend themselves to only one interpretation. In our experience, forcing an interpretation for each of the four categories is helpful, however, for we are not hunting for the sole correct interpretation. There is always the possibility that interpretations from all four vantage points may be valid simultaneously, since most behavior is overdetermined.

Now let us consider the four possible interpretations of any statement in more detail: The first is that of simple content, the face value of the words uttered by the patient. The content meaning is the commonest unit of exchange in ordinary social conversation and is usually quite obvious. The second interpretation is concerned with the feeling or affective components expressed; each statement is assumed to be accompanied by some particular feeling or complex of feelings. The tone of voice contributes heavily to making the interpretation relevant to feeling. The third analysis deals with the dynamic implications of the statement. The term dynamic is employed here with a very broad and inclusive definition. Each statement is presumed to be somehow related to and revealing of the patient's past interpersonal experiences and current personality organization. The dynamic interpretation will tend to agree with, negate, alter or add to our knowledge as expressed in the dynamic formulation. The fourth interpretation of any statement seeks to reveal the transference message which it contains. The term transference, as previously noted, is also broadly defined and includes all aspects of the relationship between the patient and the therapist. The transference interpretation is the message for or about the therapist and pertains to the relationship existing between therapist and patient. Viewed correctly, this is not a specific or unique class of interpretations but is rather the reflection of the patient's personality directly or indirectly in his relationship with the therapist. The transference interpretation has a dynamic core and feeling tone and is a contemporaneous expression of the patient's difficulties. Often the only difference between the dynamic interpretation and the transference interpretation is that in the latter the object is clearly the therapist. On other occasions the distinction between the dynamic and the transference interpretations may become much more clear-cut.

The business of the therapist is to perceive and respond to these various possible interpretations in his interactions with the patient. His capacity to do so and his comfort in doing so will be enhanced only through his increased understanding and experience. We suggest that, in reviewing a recorded interview, one should stop at the end of the patient's statement, but before hearing the therapist's response. The therapist then makes a complete analysis of the statement, as outlined above, and then formulates the response which he believes would be most effective or useful and specifies why he believes this to be the case. In so doing he takes into consideration his theoretical orientation, the dynamic formulation and the goals of therapy. The next step is to listen to the therapist's actual response as it was recorded during the hour. The response is classified as representing one of the categories which will be defined later and is evaluated against the criterion of whether it is in accord with previously stated planning or is otherwise defensible. When the therapist considers the statement to have been nontherapeutic, he makes an attempt to understand his own motivation for making the statement. The classification scheme for the therapist's response involves substantially more categories than the four employed for the patient's statement. He may respond to any of the four interpretations described for the patient's statement or he may do a variety of other things. He may not respond at all or may make a simple continuing statement. He may give advice or reassurance. He may respond in a manner which is irrelevant or is expressive of a problem of his own. It is not our intention to make value judgments as to the relative desirability of various types of responses. We believe that the desirability of a response is determined by the needs of the individual patient, the theoretical orientation of the particular therapist, the goals of therapy and the strategy of the particular therapist. We strongly believe, however, that each statement is either therapeutically desirable for a reason that can be stated clearly, or that it is an error. After considering his own response the therapist then listens to and analyzes the patient's next statement, endeavoring at the same time to study the effect of his response on the patient's ensuing statement.

While therapy hours may be reviewed in this manner by the therapist alone, it is preferable to have supervision at least periodically. The thorough review of one therapy session frequently demands a number of hours. Ordinarily such extensive supervision by a senior therapist is simply not available. Mutual peer supervision can generally be arranged for, however, and is a very satisfactory supplement to the supervision given by a more experienced therapist. The principal source of difficulty in establishing workable plans for either expert or peer supervision lies in overcoming one's initial reluctance to exhibit his own efforts. Apparently many therapists are secretly quite ashamed of their abilities, for time after time we have seen resistance expressed through an inability to get the tape recorder to function or a curious tendency to lose recorded tapes. If one can break through this initial reluctance, however, reviewing recordings of one's own therapy efforts becomes extremely rewarding and quickly broadens one's horizons.

This, then, is an overview of the system. The remainder of the book will be devoted to the explication and examination of the system and its ramifications in greater detail.

Chapter III

GENERAL ATTITUDE TOWARD THE PATIENT

IN THIS chapter we will turn our attention toward the therapist's attitudes toward people, their problems, their inadequacies, their mistakes and their capacity for change. Our purpose is to express and emphasize two requirements regarding therapists and the therapeutic process. We do this because of a belief that these basic requirements are frequently given no more than lip-service and yet are of an order of importance which cannot be over estimated.

The first of these requirements is that one must genuinely like people, not only to the extent of feeling positively toward them with their "symptoms," but positively enough that one can eschew moral judgments and can bear the brunt of relating to them. The second requirement is that one must believe that people can change. The therapist must have a deep conviction that the personality attributes of the individual, his ways of dealing with people, indeed even the earthly destiny of the individual may be alterable. Almost everyone attempting to do therapy would claim that he basically likes people and believes that they can change. However, it has been surprising and unsettling to arrive at the conclusion that some people who have done therapy for many years do not appear, in personal conversation with colleagues, to have much respect for people or for their potential for change.

Given the requirements that a therapist needs to feel positively about people and to hold the belief that they can change, how may one judge the presence of these qualities in one's self? Unfortunately, it is difficult to engage in the depth of self scrutiny necessary to evaluate these factors with validity because to do so cuts to the heart of one's own dynamics.

In an attempt to assess capacity for positive regard, we might ask ourselves: To what extent am I able to achieve positive relations in my non-therapeutic functioning? Are there a number of people I can think of whom I really like? Are there a number of people who really like me? Am I able to develop the deep warm glow that is experienced as a result of a real human contact? Am I able to experience the feelings that other people have in various situations both directly and vicariously? Are these experiences frequent? While these questions appear superficial, the results of detailed self-examination in these areas will be very helpful and meaningful.

Feelings about the capacity of people to change may frequently be evaluated by considering feelings about one's own capacity to change. Sometimes pessimism about change may be traced to personal difficulties which have not been easy to modify. If one has made a valiant effort to change himself and failed, with or without therapy, it becomes more difficult to believe that others may achieve change. However, life abounds with ample evidence that people do change, often in a most dramatic fashion. Most of us can really appreciate this in our own lives by looking back toward specific occurrences or relationships that basically altered our feelings about ourselves.

If, as a result of a searching self-examination, one concludes that basically one does not think very much of people or does not honestly believe that people can change, he should recognize that this is likely to preclude a satisfactory or satisfying therapeutic career. This would be a clear indication that one ought to shift his occupational focus to another field of endeavor, or that he ought to seek personal therapeutic help. We would consider the latter solution to be vastly superior, since the same factors that interfere with becoming a good therapist are likely to introduce difficulty in all interpersonal relations.

The beginning therapist will usually decide, after careful

thought, that he does possess the necessary attributes and will begin his first treatment case with a feeling of enthusiasm and excitement. A variety of factors, such as the limitation of time and skill, the type of patients available and the sheer difficulty of the task, not infrequently turns his feelings into those of frustration and ineptitude. The gap between the needs that he can perceive and the results that can be accomplished is enormous. It is important to realize that periods of pessimism and discouragement during the process of learning therapy are universal, rather than exceptional. Eventually one's skills improve and one acquires reasonable standards against which he can judge his achievements.

Even if one feels positively toward most people, certain patients will have qualities that are objectionable to the therapist. If this is true to the extent that one's feelings toward the patient are not generally positive, one should proceed most cautiously in attempting therapy with him. Cultural differences between the therapist and the patient may be so great that the therapist is unable to develop the depth of comprehension necessary to allow genuinely positive attitudes. There are also times when a patient's particular combination of qualities arouses feelings which are dynamically determined by unresolved areas of conflict in the therapist. Again, this is not to be regarded as shameful but it is a stumbling block if one is unaware of or unwilling to admit the negative reaction to the particular patient. We feel strongly that a therapist ordinarily should not undertake therapy with any patient who arouses strong negative feelings in himself. Therapy in such circumstances is unlikely to help the patient very much, and there is rarely a shortage of patients with whom the therapist's time would not be better spent.

Another attribute that is necessary in a good therapist is frequently assumed without mention—that of honesty. To comment on this may again seem trite and unnecessary, but experience indicates that while therapists can verbalize the desirability of honesty, insufficient regard is frequently devoted to practicing the concept, especially with the patient.

A very common if not universal problem in the emotionally

disturbed is that they have great difficulty in establishing trust in other persons. Often the people who have figured significantly in their past lives have not been trustworthy. Their lack of trust is only a reasonable result, under the circumstances.

However, for a patient to benefit from psychotherapy he must trust the therapist enough to place himself in a position of substantial dependence on the therapist. This poses a basic dilemma for the patient. He does not really trust anyone, yet he must trust an unfamiliar person in order to receive the help that person has to offer him. Under these circumstances it is not surprising that a patient will be looking for any evidence, no matter how minute, of dishonesty and untrustworthiness in the therapist.

While acknowledging the desirability of honesty, one must recognize that the temptation for the therapist to be less than completely honest may be substantial. The patient is usually at some disadvantage both in finding proof of dishonesty and in penalizing it by the various usual means. The customs of the therapist's non-therapeutic world, where a "white lie" may be acceptable, tend to carry over into his therapeutic world. Occasions are certain to arise when it appears that the treatment would proceed more smoothly if the patient were given some impression not strictly in accord with the facts. Thus, the opportunity to "manipulate" the patient with less-than-truthful management may seem to be very attractive.

How then can the therapist convince the patient of his trustworthiness? By and large, telling the patient of his honesty is not particularly effective. One must live these qualities, often for very extended periods of time, before a person who has been unwilling to admit of their possibility will accept them. One should be aware that many things which are of minor import to the therapist will be of critical significance to the patient. If, for example, we agree to write a letter for a patient this week and for some perfectly legitimate reason do not do it, the patient may view the omission as still another example of betrayal and untrustworthiness. Similarly, the failure of the therapist to be punctual for an appointment, in spite of the patient's problems in this area, might impress the patient as a failure to be trustworthy. Answers to simple questions must be carefully considered in relation to the dimension of honesty. A patient may, for example, inquire as to whether something he said made the therapist angry. The immediate reaction would be to deny anger, perhaps to ourselves as well as to the patient. But if we are angry it is likely that the patient will either know it or be able to hazard an educated guess that it is so, based upon our facial expression, tone of voice and other cues. Our denial will then either convince him that we have not told the truth or will confuse him and make him doubt his judgment of people.

One may also lie by omission. If we neglect to tell a patient that we had a long telephone conversation with his wife since the last visit, we cannot claim to be keeping him reasonably informed. Since we can never tell a patient every thought or bit of knowledge which we have in relation to him there obviously must be some selective factor. Perhaps as a guide one should report everything that could reasonably be called for in the context of the particular situation and hope that one's judgment of reasonableness coincides with the patient's.

The most difficult and perplexing problems concerning honesty arise in relation to friends and relatives of patients. One may be asked to continue a family lie to the patient in order to save the family's self-esteem. One may be asked to receive information (usually presented as being of vital importance) with the understanding that the source or the information itself will be withheld from the patient. Long experience has led us to a rather rigid position. We will never agree to tell a lie to our patient, no matter how minor and no matter who else has told the same lie. Our relationship with the patient is completely confidential and no information is released to anyone without the patient's express permission; nor is any information from other sources received in confidence. All other persons are informed that anything they say may, at our discretion, be repeated to the patient with specification of the source of the information.

The relationship between the trainee and his supervisor, particularly the honesty within the relationship, is worth a digression at this point. The trainee is in conflict. On the one hand he wishes to create a desirable impression of his skill and therefore tends to present a favorable view of his efforts, minimizing discussion of errors and problems; on the other hand he wants to learn and realizes that he most needs to learn in those areas where his performance is poorest. The supervisor is oriented toward teaching and is usually limited to discussing those aspects of the therapy that the trainee reveals to him. He will be concerned with inadequacies and errors regardless of the good qualities of the therapy, since that is his role. The trainee is frequently troubled because he is criticized even when he presents the best aspects of what he has done. This enhances his reluctance to bring out the worst features. Secretly he tends to be ashamed of what he does and finally conceals both his therapy and his shame. The situation is particularly unfortunate since experience under supervision is almost always limited and is available for such a minor segment of one's therapeutic career. This problem is best solved by mutual effort and understanding between student and supervisor. Most beginning therapists believe that their efforts are of poorer relative quality than is really the case.

One's general attitudes of regard, optimism and honesty are probably the most important aspect of treatment yet the most difficult to describe, and are not easily communicable in the ordinary pedagogic sense. Meticulous attention to detail, like that considered in the discussion of honesty, is likely to help. Everything one does should be considered in relation to the extent that it is likely to demonstrate the honesty and trustworthiness of the therapist. Every aspect of our contacts with the patient should demonstrate that we respect him, that he is a responsible human being and that we will deal with him in a forthright manner. It is this aspect of treatment that makes liking the patient important. The particular ways that we accomplish this are highly individual, varying both with therapists and with patients, and it would be misleading to indicate that certain procedures are the best ones. However, an example might be of some help at this point. It is important to take this example only as a guide to the types of things that one should consider and solve in a highly personal manner. The attempt is to illustrate the large number of variables that one must consider in learning therapy.

We have selected the initial visit in a child guidance clinic for our example since difficulties in quickly transmitting one's positive feelings toward the youngster and his parents and in effecting a smooth separation between parent and child are quite common. We have further narrowed our sights to include only those aspects of the initial visit that have to do with the period between the arrival in the clinic and the parents coming into one's office. This will serve as an example of the type of details that merit serious consideration. Since habits that are formed during one's early experiences as a therapist tend to be most enduring and to become progressively more difficult to change, attention to minute details of practice early in one's experience can have gratifying and long lasting effects.

Prior to their arrival the parents have received a definite appointment through the mail. This is done even if there has been a preliminary arrangement over the telephone. The letter provides a tangible bond to the clinic and clarifies the parent's conception of the arrangements for the visit. Although these appointments are sent far in advance, no reminder is sent out, there being an assumption that the parents are capable people and will be able to keep the appointment. At the same time there is the additional assumption that the appointment is a highly significant event for the family. Initial appointments are always worded in a manner which includes both of the parents as well as the child. If a question about the need for the father to attend is raised we stress our desire to see the whole family. This helps to provide an initial hint to our orientation and concern with understanding the total family life in relation to a child's problems. Sufficient time is set aside for the contact to make the patient's needs the determinant of how long the family will be seen.

We recognize that the parents, as well as the child, will almost certainly be feeling somewhat anxious and uncomfortable upon their arrival. The receptionist is aware of the patient's name, age, sex and appointment time, and greets the family by name. This makes them feel welcome, allays their anxiety about being in the right place at the right time and again helps to transmit our feeling about their dignity as human beings. Our willingness to memorize their names in advance also serves this purpose.

The receptionist then indicates a waiting area, points out the coat rack and indicates that the doctor will be with them in a few minutes.

The visit begins on time. However, before introductions are made the family is allowed time to acclimate itself to the waiting room with the belief that this will reduce anxiety and facilitate separation of parent and child. The delay is quite brief but appears to be significant in contributing to the degree of comfort they achieve.

If a number of persons are waiting to be seen we have the receptionist indicate the correct ones. The family is approached in a pleasant and forthright manner. If it is not awkward the examiner begins by keeping one of the parents between himself and the child, enabling the child to obtain a minimally threatening initial view. Generally we first introduce ourselves to the father. The introduction always includes his name as well as our own, such as "Hello, Mr. Smith. I'm Dr. Jones." This again serves to remove a possible source of confusion. We then offer to shake his hand, being mindful of the fact that he may be too anxious, embarrassed or confused to do so. Being aware of this possibility enables us to be prepared to withdraw our hand if indicated. Sometimes the husband will follow this by introducing us to his wife. If not, we then turn to her and introduce ourselves. Since some women expect to shake hands, we should be ready to either shake hands or not, behaving in a fashion which would serve to avoid embarrassment for her.

After completing our introduction to the parents, we turn to the child. It is preferable to get down to his level physically, so that we are looking horizontally at each other. This is one of a group of things that are small but are so rarely done with children that they have an effect far out of proportion to what we might expect. The child is greeted by name, "Hello, John. I'm Dr. Jones." We then hold out our hand. Should the child offer the wrong hand, we shake it without comment. If he does not respond we withdraw our hand without comment. He is likely to be surprised but genuinely pleased with this maneuver. The child is not patronized or talked down to.

The usual next step is to acquaint the child with the fact that we want to talk to his mother and father first while he has a chance to play. This indicates that we will also want to talk with him, although not in a manner that he can argue with, and hints that we will want to see him alone. If the mention of play is done effectively it will arouse his curiosity and interest. The child is then definitely told that the conversation with the parents will take a long time. This is a most unusual statement for the child to hear. It has been his prior experience that a similar situation produces a statement to the effect that the subsequent procedure will take only a few minutes. This cue invariably means that what follows will appear to take an eternity. The truth is that the visit will be long and the child's perception of it will be even longer, and it is only honest to say so.

It is then natural to suggest that we would like him to be able to pass the time pleasantly by having some toys to play with. A toy closet is pointed out and he is told that he may select what he wants and is invited to accompany us to the closet. By so doing, interest is expressed simultaneously with the achievement of an initial separation under circumstances that very few children will turn down—that is, going to a toy closet to pick out toys for play. If the parents evidence a desire to accompany him this is firmly but subtly discouraged, since we believe that this separation will facilitate the next one. In the toy closet we allow the child to pick what he wants without hurrying him. We may make suggestions if he appears confused or overwhelmed, but try to communicate our interest and full attention. In our experience if we can really take a relaxed attitude it is rare for more than a minute to elapse in the closet before a selection is made.

If, after returning to the parents, we judge that his anxiety level is such that separation may pose problems we offer to show him the room where his parents will be seen, and take him to the office. This is an intermediate type of separation, in a further effort to improve our relationship. He is then helped into a seat of suitable size and encouraged to become involved with the toy. We attempt to place ourselves between the child and parents to facilitate the separation. If anxiety is still a problem, we ask the receptionist to entertain the child as long as is necessary.

To avoid confusion we lead the way to the office door, which has been left open. Gesturing in a definite manner we invite the parents in saying, "Won't you come right in and take any seat?" This is to avoid a common feeling that we might wish to assign definite places to them. Rather than plunge right into the interview, we allow a brief period of time for the parents to acclimate to the office. If the pause is awkward the therapist might occupy himself with getting out a pencil and paper, lighting a cigarette or performing another routine chore. Careful observation will indicate when the parents are ready to proceed.

The same minute attention to detail should apply to all aspects of our work. If we send a letter to a patient we should be sure that the form, the content and the preparation are professional. We should carefully consider the possible effect on our therapeutic efforts. We should also wonder whether our office provides the proper atmosphere. Is the furniture suitable? Are there severely distracting elements? Does the patient experience privacy? Is one's dress such as to indicate a professional attitude and respect for the patient? In these and many other ways, one is constantly communicating his most basic attitudes toward his patients. Some therapists object to approaching patient contacts in such meticulous detail, feeling that it will interfere with their naturalness. Nonetheless, the new therapist should give some thought to what he communicates when he "naturally" arrives coatless, late, and greets the wrong patient.

In order that the more formal aspects of therapy can proceed satisfactorily a number of administrative details have to be arranged. The management of these details is frequently very uncomfortable for the beginning therapist. There is a feeling that only direct psychotherapy is really relevant and that other details smack of a non-professional commercialism and are to be avoided. One must keep clearly in mind, however, that the management of the details is as revealing of the therapist's attitude as is his management of more "therapeutic" endeavors. Since handling these necessary details is difficult for some therapists it is easy for them to rationalize the lack of necessity to deal with them. The rationalization usually takes the form of a tacit assumption that the rules and customs of therapy are common knowledge and do not have to be discussed.

The administrative details are not understood in advance by the majority of patients. Further, dealing with such details in a forthright manner, since they are reality factors in life, is therapeutic. This is particularly true when one considers the probable anti-therapeutic effects of mutual misunderstanding which might otherwise arise.

The initial administrative details are handled prior to the first appointment. Typically, this consists of obtaining the patient's name, address, telephone number and perhaps information from the referring agent and giving the patient a specific appointment. The patient comes to the first interview with a great deal of concern about his emotional problem and usually has a good deal to say. We therefore recommend that further administrative details be deferred until close to the end of the first session, unless the patient raises questions about such details earlier.

A number of details should be clarified, most of these during the course of the first visit. Any arrangements are subject to revision, of course, but the possibility that revisions might occur is not sufficient reason to ignore these details. Indeed, if a logical decision cannot be made with respect to an important question, this should be stated quite frankly.

The most obvious arrangement to conclude within the first

hour is the plan for the next visit or the decision that there will be no further visits. The exact date, time and place (if different than the site of the original visit) should be clearly specified. Psychotherapists tend to mean fifty minutes when they employ the word hour; this may be confusing or annoying to the patient and should also be explained.

The type of commitment which is being made should be clarified. This will vary in individual cases, obviously. Sometimes, for a variety of reasons, the patient will not be seen after the first visit. It is also quite reasonable to defer a decision on a protracted course of treatment until after an additional visit or series of visits. One might say, "The problem appears to be one that is going to take some time to understand. Could we plan to have about six visits, after which we will review where we are? We could then decide whether it appears desirable to go on." An alternative would be to come to an agreement for regular therapy with no definite end point. These decisions should, of course, be mutual. The therapist will most likely have to suggest the course of action, but this should be genuinely congruent with the patient's desires.

General rules or policies about the conduct of therapy should also be clarified, either early in treatment or when the appropriate occasion arises. The question of lateness for appointments should be discussed. The usual custom is for the hour to terminate at the normal time even if the patient comes in late. If this is stated either in the beginning or when the patient is late the first time it will clear the air. Similarly the provisions for cancelled or failed appointments should be specified. Vacations should be discussed, particularly if the therapist will be missing appointments because of a vacation in the immediate future. Of course, the fees should be reviewed in advance. The expense of psychotherapy is a burden for most people; prior knowledge of what will be entailed facilitates planning and certainly helps avoid unfortunate misunderstandings.

Frequently, the patient will raise difficulties concerning the arrangements for therapy in a fashion which is quite difficult to handle. Often the beginning therapist is likely to be too accommodating in making his arrangements, and will make arrangements which are uncomfortable for himself. This cannot help but lead to hostility on his part later. In general, objections to arrangements suggested by the therapist should be examined carefully before being accepted.

One should also examine the possibility that the patient's difficulties in making arrangements are a form of resistance. Resistance tends to be conceived of as a mystical entity having little touch with reality. In fact, the substance of the patient's resistance is based upon reality considerations, and is expressed through the reality situation. Everyone has at one time or another fulfilled obligations under extremely difficult circumstances, when he so desired. Real practical difficulties may arise, however, because the patient has not been honest with those around him about his entering therapy. The therapist should enter this area in the same way he would any other therapeutic situation, being especially careful not to solve these practical problems for the patient.

An important point to be considered throughout the opening stages of therapy during which administrative aspects are an issue, is the fact that the patient has come to an important and very difficult decision to seek help about his problems. He generally is uncomfortable and ambivalent about doing this and about the dependency position he may feel it imposes on him. Many of these feelings may be expressed indirectly through his reactions to the problems of administrative details. Handling these feelings therapeutically can be an excellent first step toward a good therapy relationship.

Every patient in therapy discloses some facts about himself which cause him to be uncomfortable. For this reason confidentiality is an issue. It is our custom to inform the patient that anything discussed in the hour will be held in absolute confidentiality and that if the therapist wishes to divulge information it will only be with the patient's specific permission. The patient is also told that he will be informed if anyone else contacts the therapist in reference to him and that this information will include the substance of the communication. This type of arrangement protects the therapist from unbelievable complications of intrigue, secrecy and manipulations.

In summary, the general philosophy to be followed is that administrative details need to be reviewed in an open and frank manner with the patient. Such details are an intrinsic part of therapy and should be managed in a manner which contributes to the patient's treatment.

In this chapter we have attempted to discuss the general attitudes that one should have toward patients. We indicated that this must include a positive regard for people as well as a deep conviction that people will change. A deep sense of honesty is another critical requirement. Having these basic attributes we may proceed to explore various means of communicating these feelings to the patient. The general approach involves meticulous consideration of every minute aspect of the treatment situation in relation to the individual patient and his needs.

Chapter IV

THE DYNAMIC FORMULATION

When one examines the personalities of most persons with emotional problems, it frequently appears that they are victims of their own patterns of living. Their anxiety is not based on an external reality but rather upon some inner logic which is not apparent to the casual observer. The various security operations which they have evolved for dealing with sources of discomfort are at best self-limiting and are frequently clearly self-destructive. The most bizarre and self-immolating symptoms may be the most resistant to change. Perhaps the apparent lack of logic in the formation and maintenance of symptoms played a significant role in the historical evolution of the concept of possession by either mystical demons or noxious agents. It made little sense to believe that anyone would choose to suffer or that thoughts and ideas alone could produce aberrant behavior.

Lest we scoff too readily at the archaic concept of possession, it is desirable to note that there are some aspects of the concept of possession which are strikingly parallel to our current concepts of mental illness. Almost all schools of personality theory attribute the source of difficulty to a force which is external to the conscious mind. All theoretical approaches appear to lack clarity concerning the extent to which a person has control over the expression of symptoms. For practically all systems of psychotherapy the removal of the difficulty depends upon participation in an institutionalized set of exchanges with an authority figure. In the evolution of approaches to the management of the mentally ill, the tendency to treat with compassion and kindness far antedates all of our dynamic concepts.

However, there are some novel elements in our current conceptions about mental illness. The modern view that mental illness arises as a reaction to prior life experiences is a consequence of the immense revolution which Freud introduced. The introduction of the concepts of the unconscious and of unconscious motivation made it possible to conceive of the particular personality traits and symptoms which an individual manifests as consequences of an explainable and understandable chain of circumstances; a person's behavior can be seen as his only logical choice, provided one understands his logic and the circumstances which he has experienced.

For many of the current approaches to the art of psychotherapeutic intervention, one of the most crucial ingredients is an understanding of the determinants which underlie the patient's behavior. Many terms have been applied to the end products of the various attempts to achieve this understanding. We shall use the term dynamic formulation, by which we mean a description of the current mental status of the patient, a delineation of his conflicts and defenses and an attempt to understand his difficulties through a reconstruction of the circumstances which have led to the current situation. Although we recognize that the term dynamic formulation is frequently employed with a narrower and more precise definition, we prefer to be more inclusive and to have the dynamic formulation constitute the fullest expression of all of our knowledge about the patient.

The dynamic formulation may be conceived of as an attempt to understand that which initially appeared inexplicable, to comprehend the logical series of events leading to the current difficulties. In this context, native endowment and physical health are seen as events which may have profound influence on personality development. There is a tendency for psychotherapists to minimize the contribution of these factors and to overlook the extent to which they inevitably influence interpersonal relations.

Changing the frame of reference may clarify our concept of the dynamic formulation. Consider the analogy to the task of a novelist. The novelist attempts to create real persons with words on paper. These people must have a genuine quality, must ring true, must be believable. Each character must behave in a manner which is consistent with the personality which has been established for him. A second quality which a good novelist must develop in his characters is that of depth. Rather than being heroes or villains, sane or insane, the characters must be persons, each unique, each human and capable of arousing empathy in the reader. Writing a dynamic formulation poses very similar tasks.

Among the many functions of a formally prepared dynamic formulation, facilitation of the development of empathy ranks high. The achievement of understanding about the nature and antecedents of the patient's difficulties leads to greater clarity in one's comprehension of his state of mind and feelings. An important first step in the development of empathy is often that of attempting to parallel the feelings and experiences of the patient with one's own feelings and experiences; this step leads to a form of empathy through analogy. From this it is hoped that a truer form of empathy will emerge, in which one sees the patient both as an individual and as a member of the human race, sharing the human condition.

Granted that we are all trying to understand the patient, to share his feelings and to help him, one still must recognize that if two therapists were confronted with the same patient they would sometimes evolve quite different formulations about him. Many of these differences might arise from important theoretical differences in orientations toward therapy. Even within a given "school" of therapy, it appears that different individuals become attuned to and focus upon different aspects of the personality, each seizing upon those aspects which he finds important and understandable. At times, of course, certain formulations may simply be wrong and can be proved so by the accumulation of more detailed knowledge. To a considerable extent, however, different therapists may be explaining different pieces of the same phenomenon, each explanation being valid and enabling the therapist to be of value to the patient. Also, since all behavior is probably overdetermined the question as to the "real" explanation is not germane; there are many.

It is important that each therapist evolve for himself an orientation which appears both theoretically sound and personally meaningful. Whatever the orientation, it is most important that a dynamic formulation be meaningful to the therapist who is trying to use it. It must serve to facilitate his understanding of the events which transpire in psychotherapy, rather than to provide an intellectual wall which keeps him from making emotional contact with his patient. It is equally necessary that one maintain flexibility. The formulation should fit the patient rather than the converse. Formulations must vary infinitely, as do people. If one begins to find that all of his dynamic formulations are similar, he must wonder if he is not forcing people to fit into his own preconceived notions.

The question now becomes that of how one actually produces a dynamic formulation which captures his understandings about the patient. In an attempt to make our approach to this task as explicit as possible, we shall first discuss some general issues which we feel to be important in the production of the formulation, then we shall discuss the classes of material which form its content, and finally we shall present specific examples of dynamic formulations with critical comments about them.

We strongly believe that it is necessary to write the dynamic formulation as a formal document. The written word is often a critical test of the viability and soundness of one's ideas. Formulations which are not written tend to be vague and as such are difficult to test or improve. They are also likely to suffer the handicap of concentrating on the obvious. While a written formulation is demanding of time and effort, we believe that the expenditure is amply justified.

Further, it is suggested that one use as little special and technical terminology as possible. The therapist is not dealing with structures and concepts, but with people. The avoidance of technical language is one means of helping to attain this end.

At first glance this might suggest a somewhat gratuitous disregard for the hard-won insights of dynamic theories; on the contrary, our hope is that by translating these terms into simple language one will be led to examine the patient with more care than would otherwise be the case. In addition, we would hope that such a translation would appreciably deepen one's understanding of the strengths and weaknesses of his thinking and of the theoretical conceptualizations with which he is familiar. Many times theoretical concepts are reified and personified, and eventually are endowed with wills, goals and purposes of their own. The language thus introduced tends to obscure a vast amount of ignorance while purporting to explain mental structures and functions. Finally, framing one's thoughts in everyday language may facilitate communications with the patient and may avoid the teaching of a new defensive language to an intellectualizing patient.

The difficulty involved in producing a dynamic formulation frequently leads to a series of rationalizations by the therapist which serve to postpone or eliminate the task. The beginner almost invariably finds himself to be without ideas and seriously doubts that he knows anything about people. Working out a formulation in the face of the anxiety which is aroused requires determination and intellectual honesty. It is easy to understand the tendency to postpone the task; however, since the purpose of the formulation is to provide a structure for the course of treatment, the initial formulation should be written quite early, probably no later than the third or fourth hour.

We must recognize that a dynamic formulation which is written early in one's experience with a patient will have many inadequacies. Areas of uncertainty will occur with respect to some aspects of functioning about which one has neither information nor a solid basis for conjecture. It is usually well to indicate such deficiencies in order to draw attention to what may become significant areas for later exploration. There will be other areas about which one can conjecture and offer some hypotheses which can be evaluated in the light of subsequent experience with the patient. When there are very large areas of uncertainty in presumably critical areas of the formulation, one is confronted with the necessity of recognizing this lack of information as a phenomenon of the therapy. There are at least four possible reasons for incompleteness in the material presented by the patient; each of these suggests its own solution. (1) The material may be of great importance to the patient and pertinent to his problems, but is a source of anxiety to him and is either repressed or avoided. (2) The patient may not have discussed this material because it is of little current interest to him. (3) It is possible that we have not inquired about this area of functioning and its relevance to his problems is not apparent to the patient. (4) There is a possibility that the therapist has discouraged the patient from introducing certain problems in the treatment. The therapist is well advised to consider the inadequacies of the material presented by his patient in the light of these possible reasons and to decide if there is an indication that he should do something about these inadequacies.

When considering the dynamic structure of personality one concept is often rather loosely applied; this is the concept of depth. This concept is frequently employed indiscriminantly to include two different phenomena—material from any period which is currently repressed and material relating to early or primitive experiences. The concept of depth is most commonly used to describe the extent to which something is repressed: that is, depth is defined as the distance of some material from consciousness or the difficulty that would be involved in restoring it to a conscious level. The other use of the term, referring to primitive or early experience, involves a somewhat different frame of reference. This dual usage contributes to a good deal of cognitive confusion. The situation is rendered even more confusing by the introduction of a third usage for depth; the therapist may employ the concept of depth to indicate the amount of inference he has used in arriving at a statement or the degree to which his statement is removed from the verbal content of the patient. While more careful specification of exactly what is being referred to by phrases like "on a deeper level," "underlying this" and "this symptom is a defense against a deeper" should reduce at least some of the confusion, chronological reconstruction of the development of the maladaptive personality leads to an even clearer appreciation of the inadequacies of our knowledge. It is an error to gloss over such inadequacies by depending upon the vaguely defined concept of depth, a concept which frequently serves only to absolve one's self from further thought and investigation.

Having discussed some general issues relevant to the production of dynamic formulations, we will turn now to some discussion of the types of information which comprise the actual formulation. The introductory element in the dynamic formulation is usually a specification of the presenting complaints and symptoms of abnormal functioning which have caused the patient to seek treatment. Frequently, some important problem which contributed to the patient's decision to seek treatment does not appear in the presenting complaints but is revealed only gradually. The complaints which are known, however, can serve as the initial basis for an introduction to the formulation. An important reason for the inclusion of the presenting symptoms is the tendency to lose sight of why the patient came for therapy, particularly during a long course of treatment. Specifications of the patient's original complaints will serve as a reminder of what was actually bothering the patient as opposed to what the therapist may have believed the central conflict to be.

The formulation should next delineate the relationship between the current life experiences of the patient and the world in which he finds himself. If one considers personality disturbances to be the consequence of distorted ways of viewing one's self and the world, it becomes apparent that the patient must be behaving in a fashion which maintains his environment as a continuing basis for the disturbance. A pattern of behavior must be sustained which will produce the type of environmental responses that confirm his maladaptive hypothesis. These patterns of behavior and response must be ferreted out and understood. Another aspect of the patient's functioning which deserves careful consideration concerns the rewards which accrue to him from the maintenance of his maladaptive behavior. These are ordinarily referred to as secondary gains. The formulation should also include a description of the patient's usual range of interactive behaviors and of their dynamic meaning. Awareness about these usually arises, in large part, from behavior in the therapy hour. This awareness can vastly improve the therapist's understanding of the patient's statements within the treatment hour and can provide indications of the manner by which they may be therapeutically handled.

The bulk of the formulation should be cast in the form of a narrative: a series of events which conveys a feeling for the evolution of the personality. This reconstruction of the patient's life from childhood to the present amounts to a specification of the causal chain of events leading to the patient's current personality organization. A well-prepared formulation includes a variety of material about the patient. Any information available to the therapist is suitable for use, but wherever possible material from the treatment hours should be used, since it has greater immediacy for the therapist. Strong attempts to support summary statements with specific examples are indicated; the inclusion of numerous examples helps to avoid excessive theorizing by the therapist, makes the document more individual, more genuine and more believable and is a real necessity for adequately depicting qualitative aspects of the patient's personality.

A variety of other information should be specifically noted if it has not fit comfortably into the narrative portion of the dynamic formulation. The operation of defense mechanisms should be specified and elaborated with anecdotal examples. The personality characteristics of important figures in the life of the patient and their relationships with him are to be included. Specific information about relations with authority, sexual relations, peer relations, occupational performance, religious practices and general habits may all contribute to the understanding of the patient. It is also worthwhile to consider the notion that one can deal with what the patient discusses, while at the same time wondering about that which is never discussed. Predictions made about unknown behavior will serve as an index of the therapist's degree of understanding as they are confirmed or negated by additional information.

It can be a serious mistake to describe a patient only in terms of his maladaptive functioning. The very concept "maladaptive" may involve unfortunate value judgments about the patient. Further, emphasizing the maladaptive aspects of functioning provides a very one-sided picture. One may view therapy as a process both for improving or extending the areas of satisfactory adjustment and for diminishing the areas of difficulty. Every person has real assets, few of which have been fully exploited. It is always worthwhile to consider and note these assets, for good therapeutic results will frequently obtain from exploration of positive aspects of personality functioning.

Finally, the formal diagnosis according to the standard nomenclature is included in the dynamic formulation. We recommend this in spite of a strong conviction about the shortcomings of formal diagnosis, but with the belief that improvement in categorization will come from those who have actively thought about it. It is often difficult to categorize a patient and many therapists resist doing so but the danger in not so doing is that of taking the easy way rather than working on each last detail relevant to the understanding of the patient.

The dynamic formulation should not be prepared and laid aside. It should be a changing document which reflects new insights gained from the relationship with the patient. As experience with the patient accumulates, the therapist will discover that certain aspects of the formulation are no longer tenable and must be eliminated or revised. Areas of uncertainty may be filled in and conjecture may be replaced by solidly established information. It is important that changes in current functioning be noted and incorporated in the formulation. The therapist must consider the aspects of the patient's problems with which he has tried to deal and with how much material the patient has attempted to work. Where is the patient most resistant to change? How is this resistance expressed?

If a dynamic formulation is adequately prepared it consumes a great deal of time; periodic revisions also consume time. We know of no satisfactory short alternatives but, as one becomes more experienced, the time necessary to prepare the formulation decreases. Eventually it is not necessary to write all of the details. However, the commonest mistake is to assume that one is ready to cut corners long before this is really true.

The following dynamic formulations are presented as examples. They are unedited and appear along the left side of the page as they were written; on the right side are supervisory comments.

These formulations are not presented as "ideal," but rather as the actual productions of trainees. Nor are the comments designed to be exhaustive but rather to deal with the formulation on the level at which it was presented. The reader is challenged to look for other ways in which the formulations might be improved, and, more importantly, to produce superior formulations of his own.

DYNAMIC FORMULATION – PATIENT O

The patient is a fourteen year old caucasian male, the oldest of three children in the family. He has a brother, eight, and a sister, two and one-half. He and the brother are children of mother's first marriage. The brother has been legally adopted by the stepfather, while O has not been.

This immediately raises an important question relating to the different treatment of the two boys which will have to be explored.

Current Situation and Reason for Entering Therapy

(1) General Problem

The most crucial current conflict as reported by both O and his mother concerns his current difficult relationship with her and some difficulty in maintaining himself at school. At home he is reported as being frequently difficult and as being argumentative.

It is not clear what you mean here. Is he difficult in that he is being argumentative? If so, this is redundant. If not, it would be helpful to delineate the specific complaints. Think in terms of examples.

He constantly attacks his younger

brother physically and verbally in a manner which the mother considers to be unprovoked.

Are these attacks related to whether mother is available? Does the mother always see the brother as the innocent one?

(2) Significant Others:

Mother has a number of physical complaints — both psychosomatic and gynecological. She is currently under a physician's care

Do we have some idea of how prominent or incapacitating her symptoms are? This doesn't create a sufficient image.

and is reported to be waiting for psychotherapy at another agency.

What are her reasons for desiring psychotherapy?

She feels that O is difficult to deal with

Vague. Specify and give examples. Why place this here, not above?

and does not relate to her.

Does she mean he does not relate positively? There appears to be a good deal of relationship, albeit negative. Perhaps she means that he does not fill her needs in some manner.

Interestingly, she reports that O seems to prefer his father to her; on another occasion he prefers his stepfather to her. O feels that she will frequently maneuver to keep him and the stepfather apart.

This demonstrates her conceptualizing the relationship in terms of preferences and favorites.

There are two crucial problems which O feels in relation to his mother.

There might be some advantage in looking at the problems more clearly in these four classes: The problems that the mother sees in herself, the problems that the mother sees in the boy, the problems the boy sees in the mother and the problems the boy sees in himself.

The first concerns where he should live

Since this is not ordinarily a decision a child may make there should be at least a brief indication at this point that he plays a role in this or a statement that this is fantasy.

and the second concerns his desire to avoid blame for her illness or for upsetting her while she is ill.

It will be interesting to discover whether this has a reality basis. That is, whether the mother attempts, subtly or otherwise, to make him feel guilty.

Stepfather

In addition to his difficulties with his mother O feels that his relationship with his stepfather is a progressively deteriorating one.

Does this imply that it was good for a while? If so the basis for the good relationship might be well worth exploring in detail. How does he feel about the difference in adoptive status?

Crucial in this perceived deterioration appears to be O's perception of the stepfather as a man who promises excessively but never delivers.

Good place for an example.

It is possible that this reflects a disappointment in Mr. C as a substitute for his father

The problem of splitting one's allegiance between a father and a stepfather is quite complex.

but it is also possible that the stepfather's behavior

Any notion what aspects of his behavior? Are you referring to his failure to deliver again?

coupled with the mother acting out

The concept of mother being one who acts out is rather casually introduced and not documented.

have rendered the situation disappointing for O.

O currently sees his father as being somewhat overwhelmed

Do you mean father or stepfather?

by the difficulties attendant upon his mother's illness and feels that his stepfather tends to bend over backwards to keep from disturbing her.

Is this a hint that O feels that his stepfather is partial toward his mother, that he feels a rivalry?

Thus the problem concerning the stepfather may be an acting out of O's relationship with his mother.

I am not clear about what is meant at this point.

Father

When O has mentioned his father it has been to contrast living conditions over the weekends with those at home. There has been little investigation of this relationship to date.

Better or worse? Economic or social? Satisfying? One should still conjecture at least a little with respect to such a crucial relationship.

Sibs

Similarly, O has mentioned his sibs only to say that they will share in his mother's ire at times. I have not gone into either of these areas to date

This sounds like an apology. It is not necessary.

because O has brought in a good deal of workable material concerning mother, school and stepfather. However, one is beginning to wonder why so little discussion of these people has occurred.

It is strange that siblings have not been discussed. I'm certain that this is not because there are no problems.

Schoolmates

O has been in difficulty in school for extorting money from smaller boys and for telling stories.

This is the first highly specific bit of behavior we hear about. What might we guess is the reason for this behavior? If we can't decide it would be possible to list alternate explanations. One could, for example, guess that he is reacting to the weakness his stepfather shows toward his mother and manifesting a desire to be strong by controlling others.

The principal of the grammar school feels that O was "crazy" and has said so to O, although he avoided the issue when he was contacted by the clinic for a discussion of O's problems.

The important thing here is O's reaction to the principal's statement, which you don't mention.

O's Behavior and Attitudes Toward Therapy.

From the beginning O's behavior has been an amalgam of good features and bad. His attitudes have been businesslike in many respects. He has discussed problems, and has sought role clarification; that is, he has sought advice and having been told that the process of treatment was not an advice giving one, he has turned to the task of bringing up difficulties and problems. On the other hand there have been clear examples of resistance in his behavior. First, he has been unwilling to set a once a week basis for his appointments and after an initial resistance to any scheduling

Related to a need for independence, or other explanation?

has agreed upon a twice a week.

Do you mean bi-weekly? (Every two weeks?)

(Part of his problem may be a residue of the way in which the therapy was presented to him—having been given this set in the diagnostic process. However, it is clear to him that I would be willing to see him on a once a week basis.) The second aspect of resistance occurred when he was able to attain a stable situation at home

You have described an unstable situation. How did it become stable? This is very germaine to understanding what is going on.

and he brought up the issue of leaving therapy. In a sense, he was convinced to remain in treatment. (This would have been an ideal time to discuss goals with him; however, it wasn't done.)

The third method of resistance he employs is ingrained in his character and is in many respects the key to part of his functioning. O's technique of responding to an interpretation which concerns some implied negative affect on his part is to deny the affect and to excuse the offender.

An example would help here. This seems to be good insight.

O's Character Structure, its Development and its Relationship to his Current Functioning.

At present the bulk of what is known about O refers to his defensive structure. He is a boy who is struggling to be involved with people, especially his parents, and one who perceives himself as feeling responsibility toward them.

Again, even brief examples are helpful. How does this manifest itself in treatment?

He feels that they will not permit him to contact them and that they are forcing him into a compliant pattern.

With his mother, implicitly he feels that she wants him only to be a "good boy." That is, one who cannot be blamed for anything. He feels that he is being tested, and is trying to prove his maturity to them but at the same time he is afraid of being rejected and punished by them. It is the expression of his own anger which is most threatening to him, and he continually denies his anger at others and attempts

Does he consciously experience anger at all?

to excuse what they have done to prevent himself from being angry. In his reactions with his mother her behavior makes the maintenance of this pattern extremely difficult and he is afraid he will express his anger so he pulls away from her but then feels guilty and responsible for her. He then resumes contact and the entire process is begun anew. His only out is to accept the role of a good boy, but it is one that he feels uncomfortable about. Simply avoiding blame is more satisfactory to him. Some of his behavior toward his mother and his sibs is clearly an acting out of his anger toward his mother

What behavior are you referring to? Examples.

for not permitting contacts with her.

His feelings about his stepfather are less clearly known. He maintains that he feels about him as he would toward a real father, but expresses primarily disappointment at his unkept promises and withdrawal from him. It is likely that he would prefer his real father, but since that is impossible, he probably does not want to lose the stepfather also. In part he feels that his stepfather is kept away from him by his mother. It seems likely that there is a good deal of repressed anger at and jealousy of the stepfather in terms of his close relationship with mother, which O is either unaware of or afraid to mention. In part both parents perceive his attempts to become involved with them as attempts to intrude upon aspects of the situation which concern only them, which in many respects they may be.

Overall, O feels in many respects impotent to affect adults and to change them, and feels that withdrawal and blame avoidance are his only available methods of behavior.

Again, I wonder to what extent he is able to experience and express these feelings.

In considering O's relationship to his father and his sibs we are entering the realm of the speculative, since he has not discussed these people. However, one might hypothesize that he feels hostility toward his father for having "rejected" him in the divorce proceedings and hostility toward his sibs in terms of their clearer relationship to both mother and stepfather.

Development of His Current Method of Functioning.

It would appear that two factors existed which resulted in O's current combination of blame-avoidance techniques and acting out proclivities. First, the confusion of being exposed to a large number of authority figures, many of them undoubtedly different in their demands on him, must have led to a feeling that the actions of authority figures are arbitrary and that one must avoid the pain of separations from them. Thus being good may have been his only defense against feeling that his movements constituted rejection.

You probably mean precipitated rather than constituted.

We have no way of knowing to what extent his being blamed for his grandmother's death is typical of his experiences but it must have created his need to avoid getting blamed for a parallel disaster occurring to his mother. Second, one gets the impression that implicitly or explicitly it was communicated to O that he was in some way to blame for his parents' difficulties. At the same time he must have been forced to deny and act out any hostile feelings he may have had toward others, for fear that recognition and expression of them would lead to further infection. As a consequence he would feel free only when there were no open criticisms expressed by others around him.

Overall this is a good formulation and holds together logically. It would benefit from specific examples to illustrate many of the points made. A more genetic frame of reference would also help.

DYNAMIC FORMULATION — PATIENT R

Mrs. R is a forty-one year old mother of two sons. She came to Child Guidance Clinic because of

—not because of but rather with the presenting complaint of. This distinction is important, since if we view *her* as our patient or one of our patients we must presume that she came because of needs of her own.

problems with the older son, B, who has congenital heart damage, partially corrected by surgery. She has trouble managing B,

One would guess, if she sees the difficulty as her own trouble with managing B, that she tends to take burdens on herself. You go on to indicate that B has trouble with everyone.

who is fearful of anticipated surgery, has insomnia, has a loud mouth and uses foul language and has difficulty in school and with father and younger brother. Mother has had a child guidance evaluation before in 1956, when B was hyperactive and aggressive toward peers. She was in treatment for a short time

A much more detailed report of previous therapeutic contact is indicated, as a guide to planning present therapy and for avoiding the same problem that led to lack of satisfactory resolution previously.

but cancelled many appointments and seemed unable to deal with her problems verbally. R was later seen for a long, not too intensive series of

See previous comment.

interviews in the Social Service Department. Why these were terminated is not clear but she has complained that all social service workers ever want to talk about is her history and they don't help her with her difficulties with B.

We may anticipate the same phenomenon in your therapy.

Mother was seen by present therapist for diagnostic studies in summer of 1961 and was followed on approximately a once a month basis from fall of 1961 until February, 1962, when once a week treatment was started.

Mrs. R is the older of two sisters. She recalls that as a child she was much closer to her father who was handsome, companionable and virile.

It would be helpful to know something more about the father to give a more rounded picture. Occupation? Education? Socio-economic level of his family? Cultural type of home? We don't get a feeling about this man.

Father seemed very adequate to her and was majorly responsible for teaching Mrs. R social graces, how to get along with boys and the facts of life.

Mother

Similar comment as for father.

was much closer to sister and provided the guidance for her that Mrs. R got from father. Mrs. R did not get along well with mother as an adolescent or as a young married woman.

What was the nature of the conflicts?

Finally, Mrs. R "read her mother off"

What is the explanation for this phenomenon? Was this an assertion of independence?

for interfering with the care of B, the first born grandson. Since that time Mrs. R and mother have gotten along with less friction but the relationship is not close. Father died of a heart attack when Mrs. R was in her early twenties.

Do we know anything of her reaction to her father's death? Thus far we are led to believe that there was a close bond and perhaps that she never had emerged from this.

She was not yet married and probably hoped to replace her beloved, idolized father with her husband. Mrs. R married at age twenty seven to Mr. R who was also twenty seven. He is a soft, gentle man who believes that wife and family are the most important focusing points for his life. Mrs. R reports that they never fight but actually they do not get along well. Mr. R is very short tempered with the boys and generally does not suit Mrs. R's ideal. She did not find a handsome, adequate father figure but rather got a soft, somewhat inadequate, uncommunicative man who is unable to resist her domination.

What is the background of the husband? You are painting a flat picture of him. Is he really unlike her father? Is her domination a result of her identification with her father or her mother? Is the short temper consistent with the "soft gentleman?"

The first son, B, was born somewhat prematurely and was diagnosed at ten days as having congenital heart damage.

Planned or desired pregnancy? Attitude of each parent to pregnancy. Any untoward events during pregnancy?

This precipitated an hysterical episode in Mrs. R.

I suspect you are using this term very loosely. What are the details of this reaction? The reaction to a gross stress is important as one indication of the type of plan one may evolve for psychotherapy.

Certainly her fantasy hopes for a son

In order to know this one must at least conjecture about her fantasy. If she has a need to dominate, a damaged child might be quite congruent with her needs.

could not be realized by this damaged baby. Her second son was born one and a half years later and was normal; he has grown up to be a healthy, aggressive, masculine boy

The question of this boy's mental health is an important one. Did the parents' difficulties become focused on

B? If so, how were the brother's needs fulfilled? Did the father take over the second boy and the mother take over B in a division similar to that which occurred in her home?

who is in conflict with B.

The nature of the sibling conflict and the parents' reaction to it would be of interest.

Much of Mrs. R's trouble in handling her son probably arises from her conflicted wishes and feelings for B. She is very guilty about her possible contribution to his prenatal damage

Commonly this guilt focuses on something specific.

and about her presumed early rejection (only hypothesized)

It would be nice to also hypothesize about the reasons for the present rejection.

and about B's early replacement by the second son.

Do we really believe that B was replaced?

She has very mixed feelings about B's current status. She is very angry about his low school achievement, his provocative behavior toward herself,

In what ways is he provocative, particularly toward her? Does she encourage this provocativeness?

father and brother; she has mixed feelings about his inadequacies as an athlete;

Is this an expression of her attitude toward virility?

she approves of his cleverness, his companionableness with her and his artistic and creative bent. She tends to handle him very inconsistently, praising him one minute and screaming at him the next.

Is there a patterning to this, or is it more of a "safety-valve" phenomenon?

She frequently compares him with her inadequate husband to Mr. R's detriment.

In what dimensions?

Presumably, the real comparison is to her lost father, whom she hopes to replace with an ideal son.

Here again I wonder about the differential attitude toward the two sons. Why not employ the second child if she wants to replace a virile father? It would appear that her relationship with B is much more intense than that with her second son.

The seductiveness which she probably showed to her father is currently being practised on B.

The present most crucial focus of her thoughts is the coming surgery which B will shortly undergo.

Is this surgery genuinely life threatening?

She is anxious and guilty about her past handling and is attempting to deny the possibility of losing B. Until after surgery, very little else can be dealt with in therapy

Although this may be correct, it is important that we do not preclude consideration of other areas because of our attitude.

since the surgery date is the bench mark for all her current feelings and concerns.

There are many areas of Mrs. R's life that we have not touched upon. What is her education? Is she intelligent? What are her assets? What is the relationship with her sister, both current and past? Does she have friends? What are her sources of satisfaction?

A large issue is the question of why she comes in the first place. Does she want something for herself? If so, does this include things unrelated to B? What diagnosis is appropriate for Mrs. R? How fragile is she?

Chapter V

GOALS OF THERAPY

THE DYNAMIC formulation, as discussed in the previous chapter, is the written representation of the therapist's attempt to understand his patient's unique personality and its evolution. Its purpose is to delineate the patient's strengths and problems as a precursor to treatment. However, our capacity to understand psychopathology far outstrips our capacity to affect it, especially in the case of the new therapist.

A number of situations both perpetuate and reflect this state of affairs. In many training centers the bulk of staff discussions centers around the diagnostic phase of the treatment process and are primarily, if not exclusively, concerned with understanding the patient's dynamics. A preponderance of theoretical papers published tend to deal with some aspect of dynamics, frequently conceptualized at a level of abstraction far removed from the realities of the therapy hour. It is as if there were a tacit assumption that a clear understanding of the patient's conflicts will automatically produce beneficial therapeutic responses.

It appears, however, that many a therapist who is able to conceptualize and formulate a reasonably coherent statement of the patient's difficulties and their genesis, is left with a feeling of inadequacy about his attempts to translate these understandings into behavior. The purpose of training programs in therapy, and the purpose of this book is to aid the therapist to utilize his dynamic understanding of the patient in a way which will produce useful therapeutic behaviors.

If one considers the array of reasons why psychotherapy may fail, they seem infinite, and in many instances hinge upon occurrences outside the control of the therapist. While no one would deny that there is a real world which can intervene to disrupt the therapeutic process, many failures derive from a deficiency in patient-therapist communication. These failures in communication can be conceptualized as relating to four classes of events.

First, the patient must be willing and able to discuss material which is meaningful and pertinent to himself or the therapist; second, the therapist must be able to understand meaningful statements when they are made; third, the therapist must respond to these statements in a useful fashion; and fourth, if the patient has produced meaningful material which has been correctly understood and usefully responded to by the therapist, the patient must be able to accept and use the therapist's responses. In this chapter, we will be concerned with one aspect of the first and third of these difficulties; we will propose that a therapist can foster the production of meaningful statements by both the patient and himself through the setting of mutually agreed upon goals for the therapeutic exchanges.

In the 1958 Webster's *New Collegiate Dictionary,* a goal is defined as follows: "(1) the mark set to bound a race; the end of a race or journey. (2) the end to which a design tends; objective; aim." We intend to use the term goal in both these senses, as a termination and as an objective. To be very specific, we believe that in successful therapy it is very useful, if not essential, that the patient and the therapist mutually decide which classes of events in the patient's life they will focus upon, and which discomforts and anxieties they will attempt to ameliorate. Somehow this direct statement has been found to be very upsetting to many therapists. One set of commentators feels that it is too cognitive an approach, inferring, apparently, that it likens therapy to an impersonal problem solving procedure. Another argument appears to be that it is superficial and that the consequences of goal setting would be a flight into health. A third objection is that it is the patient's inability to set reasonable life goals which leads him to enter therapy. Somehow one gets the impression that many persons feel that once a therapist has elected to take this step he will take leave of his clinical senses. In fact, setting goals with a patient is a very difficult and delicate matter, one requiring a knowledge of the patient's interpersonal techniques and his strengths. Nonetheless, if one assumes that the therapist will have goals he wishes to attain, and the patient will have goals he wishes to attain, the process of bringing these goals into congruence can only serve to improve communication and heighten the patient's self-respect.

The technique of goal setting has a number of concrete advantages. This process provides the therapist and his patient with an opportunity to arrive at an agreement to discuss areas of the patient's life which both believe to be important, and which the therapist believes will lead to productive exploration of basic conflicts in the patient's life. It defines the purpose of the conversations which constitute therapy and assists the patient in overcoming his initial confusion about his role in therapy, confusion which interacts with and can be mistaken for resistance. It forces the therapist to become aware of and deal with the patient's purposes in entering therapy. It demonstrates to the patient the therapist's conviction that the patient's decisions and impetus are essential to the success of the therapeutic undertaking. It can serve as a bridge between the therapist's dynamic understanding of his patient and the subsequent formulation of strategies of behavior which will serve to guide the therapist in the therapeutic interaction. Finally, explicit goal setting can lead to recognition of a variety of circumstances which tend to put limitations and constraints on the therapy plan. We will consider this last point first.

When evaluating the limitations inherent in a particular therapy situation, the first conditions to be recognized are those reality limits which are externally imposed. Because these factors often are not considered in detail, we will discuss a number of issues which can force compromise between theoretically ideal goals and the goals to be proposed for a real and individual patient.

One of the primary reality factors necessitating compromise is the immense social pressure for psychotherapeutic service. The mental health needs of the population are overwhelming; the demand has long since exceeded the capacity of the mental health professions adequately to cope with the problem through application of traditional therapeutic techniques. A resolution for this problem which has been frequently adopted, consciously or unconsciously, appears in many respects to be a neurotic one. That is, a number of therapists seem to be responding to the pressure by raising their standards of what constitutes adequate treatment and thereby usually increasing the duration of the treatment. This resolution is not as irrational as it might sound since it reflects, in part, a growing sophistication about the complexities of psychopathology; however, we will never satisfy the mental health needs of our society by devoting ourselves to the process of helping a very few people become extremely well adjusted.

In any case, the luxury of adopting this resolution is beyond the reach of most mental health workers, although the reasons tend to differ from one situation to another. The trainee or resident frequently is confronted with the necessity of dealing with patients in a setting in which there are many demands and a limited time, which precludes attaining optimal goals. The staff therapist frequently is expected to share in administrative, diagnostic, teaching and sometimes research obligations in addition to his treatment responsibilities. For the therapist in private practice, financial necessities may force compromise; given the large amount of time devoted to a single patient in therapy, fees adequate to provide a reasonable income pose an unreasonable financial burden for the average person in the population. In most situations there are limiting reality factors which the therapist must consider when defining his role with a particular patient and discussing the goals of treatment. While many limitations arise from the therapist's circumstances, other limiting conditions derive from the patient's side of the interaction. The patient's motivation for treatment will not necessarily approximate the therapist's ideal. After diagnostic evaluation the therapist may honestly and correctly believe that an extensive psychotherapeutic experience is indicated and would be beneficial. However, the patient might desire only minor changes, or might be unwilling to involve himself in the stressful and expensive effort necessary to effect the degree of change which the therapist believes would be desirable. Frequently, the stresses and pressures with which the patient is confronted in his daily life may be such that it is necessary for him to maintain his current defensive structure, unsatisfactory as it may be. This situation frequently applies in the treatment of children. In addition to limitations imposed by the patient's motivational level, limitations may also be inherent in the situation if the patient is relatively limited either intellectually or experientially and is, as a result, unable to verbalize, to conceptualize or otherwise participate in the therapeutic process as it is customarily conducted by the particular therapist.

These, as well as a variety of other limiting factors, may contribute to a considerably less than optimal therapeutic outlook for any particular patient. It is manifestly unfair to both the patient and to oneself to ignore and avoid these issues. Their resolution is, in many respects, not only a technical issue but also an ethical problem which confronts every therapist. We must ask ourselves: How shall we select our patients? Shall we treat only those who conform to our criteria for the ideal patient? Can we function effectively within the limitations imposed by the circumstances of our patient and ourself? Setting goals will not totally solve these problems but it will force the therapist to take cognizance of them.

Before he can adequately define goals of treatment the therapist must recognize that the patient initially comes to the therapist with goals of his own, sometimes very specific ones, even though he may not have formulated them as such. Generally these goals are expressions of the discomfort he feels. Among the unsophisticated, the goal which the patient wishes to pursue is frequently that of symptom alleviation; if his knowledge is more extensive, he may formulate his goals in more psychodynamic terms. Often, however, the patient's goals are not directly stated and may be very difficult to clarify. This process of goal clarification is an essential step in the therapeutic process, one which needs to be resolved for therapy to proceed. Out of this clarification and out of the dynamic formulation will emerge the mutually agreed upon goals around which therapy will be based.

We stress the patient's goals for a number of reason, not the least of which is the distinct possibility that they will be overlooked by the therapist in his zeal to plan a therapeutic course leading to an outcome which will be gratifying to himself. However, this very imposition of supposedly beneficial goals by others is frequently one of the conflict-producing situations which the patient has experienced in the past. Therefore, the experience of working cooperatively with the therapist to evolve mutually acceptable goals is an extremely beneficial experience. We believe that goal congruence is so important that if a goal desired by the therapist cannot be shared by the patient it must be deferred until he is able to share it, or it must be abandoned.

One obstacle to achieving goal congruence is the therapist's feeling that the patient's goals are merely expressions of his illness. Frequently, it appears that a therapist regards the patient's goals as superficial and insufficient to produce positive changes in the patient's adjustment. While it is true that the patient's approach to psychotherapy is often indicative of his difficulties, it can also be an expression of his strengths and of his perception of the world. However, even when the patient's goals are trivial or somewhat pathological, being willing to acknowledge and deal with them can be a significant communication of his importance in the relationship and may communicate the therapist's belief that both the force and the direction necessary for treatment must come from the patient.

If, after careful consideration, the therapist decides that some goal of the patient is impossible in whole or in part, then there should be explicit clarification of this point. The process of discussion and clarification and the resultant resolution of difficulties is therapeutic. It is often true, however, that a narrowly or concretely defined goal of the patient can be the path through which a more broadly defined goal which seems desirable to the therapist can be attained. For example, the patient's goal of "getting along with my wife" can lead to an exploration of the patient's relationship with women in general, with his mother, with other men, and to clarification of the very core of his definition of masculinity and himself. The therapist at this juncture, could simply point out that in discussing and working on the patient's relationship to his wife, these other issues will be involved. He would not be compelled to indicate that he feels that the patient's masculine identifications are faulty any more than he would be compelled to interpret a piece of behavior as having homosexual implications the first time he became aware of it. That is, it is not to be expected that all of the therapist's goals will be presented or agreed upon at one point in time. Some goals may be discussed with the patient as soon as the therapist has completed his formulation; others may be introduced much later in therapy. In the above example the discussion of the patient's masculine identity would occur at a time and in a manner which allows the patient to decide whether or not he wishes to incorporate it into the treatment. Generally such a goal may be discussed and adopted with relative ease at the point in therapy where the patient's understanding has progressed to include recognition of the difficulty toward which the goal is oriented.

One of the most important tasks the therapist has is to assign priorities to goals. One goal need not be accomplished in order to simultaneously pursue a second goal. The most clear cut example of a need for priorities arises when the patient is accepted in the middle of an acute crisis. In such cases, the therapist may decide to approach the crisis situation with a certain set of goals and to continue treatment following the crisis with a quite different or perhaps even opposed set of goals. When both short and long term goals are planned, it is particularly important that the therapist keep the proposed time sequence firmly in mind. In any case, as the therapy proceeds the patient and therapist should progress toward the delineation and discussion of more inclusive materials based upon reasonable and achievable goals.

Since the notion of setting goals appears to be contrary to

some approaches to therapy, it seems wise to include a more or less concrete discussion of how goal setting might be approached. First of all, there is the problem of when to introduce the discussion of goals in the therapy hour. One can either introduce the discussion at the beginning of the hour, or wait until a natural break occurs in the patient's introduction of material. For some inexplicable reason, the hour during which the therapist decides to introduce the discussion is often the one in which the patient chooses to talk a great deal. If this is the case the transition from what the patient is discussing to the idea of goals can be made more or less smoothly by anyone with the requisite verbal skills to become a competent therapist. Nonetheless, it appears best to introduce the idea of goals at the beginning of the hour, trusting that the patient will be able to retain any significant material until after the discussion.

The therapist can then introduce the matter in the following way, among others. "You remember when we began meeting X number of weeks ago, I said that we would get together for a few weeks to discuss some of your problems and difficulties, and to get to know each other somewhat better. We decided then that at this point we would see whether we wanted to continue. I wonder now how you feel about that." Unless the patient decides to terminate at this point, the therapist then formally agrees to continue therapy or to extend the trial period depending upon the patient's reactions. The therapist then goes on to summarize briefly his view on how therapy proceeds and how the patient can be helped, and concludes by saying something which has the effect of wondering what more or less specific issues and problems the patient would like to work on. It is important at this juncture that the therapist not supply the answer to the patient but rather draw the patient into a discussion from which they select areas of mutual agreement upon which to work. The therapist must maintain a middle ground between being trapped into the patient's view of the world or trapping the patient into his. He must in effect bring the patient's view of the world into conjunction with the approach he wishes to employ to help him.

It should be expected that it will take time to work out a suitable set of goals, and it is usually desirable to reintroduce the issue during the hour after a resolution has been reached in order to cement and re-examine the agreed upon goals. Throughout this discussion the therapist should provide a large dose of reality testing, including a careful examination of the burdens of time, money and effort which are involved.

As an aside it should be suggested that the therapist who is unconvinced of the utility of goal setting but wishes to test it should be careful to introduce it into cases which appear to be manageable as well as into cases which are posing therapeutic problems.

We will now consider how the setting of goals can diminish the obstacles cited in the introduction to this chapter. Stated positively, goal setting should help the patient to produce material which is therapeutically relevant and to guide the therapist in the development of strategies which will facilitate the patient's comprehension of the effects and significance of his behavior, with a view to modifying it.

As has been noted previously, a patient typically undertakes therapy because of a feeling of dissatisfaction with his life. Many times he begins with a feeling of desperation because of previous failures to change. He proclaims, by his decision to enter therapy, that he wants help and yet at the same time there is resistance, through which the patient expresses his fear of change and the feeling of threat inherent in re-examination of past difficulties. It is our contention that some part of what is commonly identified as resistance is due not to the patient's anxiety in the face of threat but instead arises from a failure of communication between the therapist and his patient. The new therapy patient is in an unfamiliar situation, one in which verbalizations have unusual effects which are different than those to which he is accustomed. The therapist does not respond to him as other people have and so the patterns of interpersonal behavior which the patient has learned in the past are less relevant and security-providing than usual. Thus anxiety is aroused and resistance occurs. The patient must learn the expectations and customs which obtain in the new situation; he must learn how to behave in his new role. It is our belief that the patient's progress through the difficult period of role definition can be aided considerably through the process of setting goals which he can agree upon as reasonable and toward which he can direct his behavior; he can use the focussing quality of goals as a guide in the business of being a patient in the therapy relationship.

Once goals are agreed upon, the therapist must state them explicitly for himself and for the patient. We firmly believe that the more specifically one can state the goals of therapy, the more likely one is to achieve them. This is, at least in part, attributable to the probability that if the therapist can state goals simply and explicitly, he understands them and has considered the various ramifications of the patient's problems and how he might assist the patient.

Often the requirement for explicit goals of therapy is avoided through the use of general statements which are ordinarily applicable to all patients; these can not serve as effective substitutes for more detailed formulations based upon the patient's specific and personal goals. The goals, for example, of getting to know a patient better or of forming a relationship with him are certainly valid but are most likely insufficient. Such general goals may well be necessary precursors to later progress if they facilitate the development of a therapeutic relationship within which the patient can attain his specific goals, but they are not sufficient goals in and of themselves.

As with other elements in this system for learning therapy, we believe that both the therapist's goals and agreed upon goals must be formulated in writing. When the goals are exclusively mental they tend to be even more vague than other aspects of the formulations about the patient. Putting goals into prose style is difficult; the beginner may erroneously attribute the difficulty to his lack of writing ability. Almost always the real source of the difficulty is the fact that it is hard to crystallize one's thinking about goals and to be specific. Once written, the goals are not to be considered as static. Periodic revision to accommodate changes in the situation is necessary. The most convenient occasion for revision is the periodic revision of the dynamic formulation.

Once the goals are formulated the therapist may proceed to what is often the most difficult and important task, that of outlining the methods by which he hopes to help the patient achieve these goals. The methods chosen obviously will depend upon the therapist's theoretical orientation and the nature of the goals being sought. The existence of the goals serves as a conceptual bridge between the global understanding of the patient achieved through the dynamic formulation and the concrete statements and behaviors which the therapist produces during the therapeutic hour. For example, it may be that careful consideration of a particular goal will lead to the conclusion that it may best be achieved by a long term uncovering process aimed at an exploration of early relationships. If this is the case, then the therapist's responses to the patient's statements would, in general, be oriented toward the dynamics rather than toward some other aspect of his statements. In another case one might believe that the goals are essentially interpersonal in nature and should be approached by means of analyzing the transference and other current relationships. The therapist would plan to include frequent exploration of various aspects of the transference. A third set of goals might seem to demand a directive approach with advice, suggestions and reassurance.

In general, the goals will obviously influence the selection of therapeutic techniques; further, failure to attain a particular goal by employing a particular set of techniques can lead to the decision to adopt a new approach or to re-evaluation of the goal. This re-evaluation may occur when, because the patient has not brought in materials which are useful in approaching his goal, or because of some failure in the therapist-patient communication about goals, it becomes apparent that there has been little progress. The therapist can then point out that little progress has been made (which will come as no surprise to the patient) and either point out that the patient has not been able to bring useful materials or that he, the therapist, has not been able to say things about the materials which are useful to the patient. At this point one can wonder where it is that the therapy has bogged down. This moment is liable to be an agonizing one in terms of its transference and counter-transference implications, and it is crucial that the therapist not be punitive, and be ready to understand that the patient will frequently feel that he is being punitive. Nonetheless such a situation affords an excellent and quite therapeutic opportunity for cementing the decision to work together, setting new goals or reiterating old ones, and for vastly improving the therapeutic milieu.

The achievement of a goal is worth noting explicitly. Often changes in treatment are slow and occur in imperceptible degrees rather than with dramatic suddenness. Both patient and therapist may forget how much difficulty was posed by a previous symptom which has gradually disappeared. Difficulties in verbal expression or in dynamic understanding may no longer be present. The therapist may find that playing a tape recording of an earlier hour to the patient can be an enlightening and encouraging procedure. Viewing progress can be growth-promoting in itself and can evoke enthusiasm for further progress on the part of both patient and therapist. The following examples of goals of therapy refer to the patients whose dynamic formulations are presented in Chapter IV. The format is the same, with the goals as written appearing in the left column and the supervisory comments in the right. It should be noted that these goals are those derived from the dynamic formulations, and are not necessarily the final goals which emerged from discussion with the patient.

GOALS – PATIENT O

The first goal of this treatment is to aid O in recognizing how his behavior leads to the reactions that other people have toward him. It is hoped that the development of such awareness will free him from feeling that he has no choice but to persist in attempting to avoid blame. To the extent that he understands his effect on others he should be able to understand what is producing their reactions and be free to attempt to gain openly what he wants from them.

Some would argue with this on theoretical grounds. Understanding the effect that one has on others does not necessarily lead to the ability to openly gain one's desires.

The second goal of treatment is to help him clarify what he wants, to clarify the relationship of his parents and sibs to him, and to decide what steps are needed in order to attain a satisfactory relationship with his mother.

The ultimate goal of treatment would be to help him understand how his blame-avoidance behavior developed and thus to free him somewhat from the need to utilize others as his source of direction and behavior.

The first two goals must be approached by dealing with the contemporary relationship and the transference situation; the final goal could be approached through seeking the relationships between his current responses and his past experience rather specifically.

You would find this easier to achieve if you thought through what you wanted to accomplish in greater detail.

Such exploration would be undertaken only if concentration on the current situation were to prove ineffective in changing his pattern of behavior.

The goals, in general, appear achievable and reasonable.

GOALS – PATIENT R

Short Term Goals:

(1) Provide support and an opportunity to ventilate feelings about surgery.

(2) Moderate feelings toward B's current misbehavior by helping to clarify his current anxieties and their relationship to his misbehavior.

(3) Clarify and provide alleviation of guilt about "forcing" the setting of surgery date.

The goals are clear. It would be helpful to detail some of the methods by which one hopes to achieve these goals.

Long Term Goals:

(1) Revision of expectation that B will be perfect replacement for father.

Are you saying that you want to resolve her oedipal conflict? If so, how? Or do you want to divert it away from the boy? If so, toward what and by what means? The frame of reference is in this vein.

(2) Develop consistent, appreciative handling of B as an individual, without present overlay of guilt and ambivalence.

This is complicated. How is the guilt and ambivalence to be resolved?

(3) Clarify relationship to husband and the historical basis for her difficulties with him, i.e., lack of appreciation, demandingness, sabotaging of his relationship with their sons.

(4) Develop acceptance of self as a competent but still female woman, who can tolerate fulfilling her dependency desires without being resentful of the gratifying person.

The overall comment about the goals is that they are rather sweeping, considering the particular case. Specific thought as to how these goals are to be achieved is necessary. If one is forced into the exercise of stating what one proposes to do (subject to all sorts of change) the goals should become more reasonable. It is also crucial to consider the patient's ability and desire for change.

SUMMARY

Goal formulation is accomplished through the following process: The dynamic formulation and the steps that one may take to alter its consequences are considered in relationship to the limits set by the circumstances of the relationship and the people in it. This is followed by explicit consideration of the patient's goals, and the goals sought by the therapist with the end of arriving at mutually acceptable goals. The goals, written, then serve as an aid in defining the areas of functioning to be explored and the aspects of the therapist's armamentorium which can be brought to bear on the problem. Goals are revised periodically, particularly in the early part of the therapy. During the course of therapy, attention should be drawn to goals which have been achieved. If no progress is being made in treatment a discussion of the difficulties encountered can be focused around mutually agreed upon goals.

Chapter VI

THE PATIENT'S STATEMENT

IN APPROACHING the study of psychotherapy, one should try to balance a healthy respect for the complexity of the psychotherapeutic endeavor with a realization that psychotherapy consists, after all, of two persons talking to each other; two persons having conversations which are scheduled at more or less regular intervals over a length of time.

A conversation consists of a series of exchanges between the two involved parties, exchanges which are primarily verbal. Our approach to the study of a therapy hour is to divide it into its component exchanges and then analyze each of these exchanges individually. This approach raises the issue of whether therapy consists of a series of related and roughly equivalent statements and responses, or whether it is best thought of as a mosaic of such exchanges. At present, this point is a moot one, although it would appear that this system of analyzing the individual exchanges is applicable in either case.

In this chapter we will be concerned exclusively with the patient's participation in the dialogue. More specifically, we will address ourselves to a method for studying the verbal component of his communications. Although the non-verbal aspects of therapy are important, and will be discussed in some detail later, we have excluded them from this type of analysis because most therapists lack the facilities necessary for recording sessions in a fashion which will permit detailed analysis of non-verbal communications. Second, while not denying the importance of non-verbal communications, we feel that the bulk of the clinical transaction is verbal.

In previous chapters we have conceptualized therapy from the broad viewpoint of the dynamic formulation and the goals of therapy. For the present discussion we will focus on smaller units, the single therapy hour and the "exchanges" or "communication units" which occur during that hour. In this chapter we will focus our analysis on the statements made by the patient, considering their meaning from four different frames of reference: the content; the affect; the dynamics; and the transference.

THEME OF THE HOUR

While a particular treatment hour may be viewed as but one of a linked chain of hours, the hour can also be considered as having a certain functional unity in and of itself. This unity often relates to a central theme around which many of the patient's discrete expressive behaviors are organized. Therefore, it is often helpful to consider the events of the hour in a global way in an effort to formulate a statement concerning the theme of the hour before one attempts an analysis of the specific statements made by the patient. Although this unitary quality is probably not present in all therapy hours, there is some advantage in assuming that it is present and in attempting to ferret out what the central theme has been.

Frequently, the theme of the hour will be expressed in the patient's opening statement; this is one of the reasons that it is generally considered good practice to allow the patient to open the hour. While this statement should be examined for its content, affect, dynamic and transference implications, the core theme being expressed is usually a dynamic or transference problem, and these frames of reference should be stressed in seeking the theme of the hour.

Examples

[Note: The reader will note that the subjects of the examples are the same as those employed in Chapters IV and V. There is an advantage in being familiar with that case material before reviewing these examples.]

O's first statement: "We're gonna move."

T: "Oh, you are, when?"

O: "Well, we were gonna—my dad doesn't want to move. We all want to move out to the Heights or something. Real nice place, only he doesn't want to. I was hoping we would, ah—you get sort of tired of everyday stuff, you know. Find something new."

Theme—The most immediate and obvious theme of this statement is . . . my father won't give us what we want. Here is something very exciting and he won't let us do it. This theme is a representation of one of this patient's emotional syllogisms, to wit; people who love me give me things, this person does (or does not) give me things, therefore, this person does (or does not) love me. The last part of the patient's statement relates more directly to his ascription of magic powers to adults; they can make the dull exciting, the old new. Since parents have magic powers, if they do not give things it is because they don't want to. All of these ideas have obvious transference implications, although it is not clear that these transference elements are being directly expressed in this statement.

R's first statement: "I wanted my husband to come with me today, in the worst way—but he couldn't. He needs it (psychotherapeutic help) (laughs) badly. He just doesn't think B is going to make it (through the operation) at all."

Theme—Dynamic: R wishes her husband to be strong and supportive but he is undercutting her defenses by doubting the wisdom of surgery. Her response to this threat is to deride and belittle him by implying that he really needs help and is too weak to ask for it, and thus reduces the potency of the threat.

Theme—Transference: R is asking therapist to give the support and reassurance which her husband cannot provide. She is saying—reinforce my defenses—agree with me that my husband is wrong and help me deny that my son will die.

As the hour developed, the therapist is inclined to accept the dynamic theme as more central.

The theme of the hour is not the substantive issue which is discussed, but the underlying pattern of defenses and conflicts which is unearthed by a substantive issue. Thus, patient O may not return to a discussion of the new house, but might instead mention receiving a lower grade than he should have obtained, or complain about his allowance. All of these remarks have in common the notion that magically powerful adults are not giving to him, and it is this interpretation which is the theme of the hour.

The theme of the hour can be best conceptualized as a strand which holds many, but not necessarily all of the patient's productions together. The patient will not necessarily discuss only material having to do with the theme of the hour, but will return to it throughout his productions. Some patients, especially the more intelligent, more complex patients will have more than one theme in an hour, and may interweave them. Finally, there are patients who characteristically introduce significant material late in the hour. The therapist should be aware of this tendency but should also wonder about the extent to which prior productions are used to build up to the final theme.

THE COMMUNICATION UNIT

For the purposes of analyzing the specific verbal interactions of a treatment hour, we divide the hour into the individual verbal exchanges which occurred between the patient and the therapist. These exchanges are called communication units; communication units are defined in terms of the natural pauses that occur in the verbal flow. By a natural pause, we mean an interruption in the verbal flow which might ordinarily be considered to indicate the end of a remark and which frequently may imply the expectation of some response.

The patient's segment consists of everything that the patient has said from the beginning of a statement until there is a natural pause, whether or not the therapist replies, or until the therapist interrupts the patient. If the therapist should interrupt a patient, the patient segment is completed at that point. Often patients will make prolonged statements, sometimes lasting a number of minutes. Even a very long statement is considered to be a single communication unit; however, if the unit is long and complex it may be subdivided at convenient intervals for the purpose of analysis.

The therapist's task is to analyze each of the patient's segments from each of four conceptual viewpoints—the content, the affect, the dynamic, and the transference. Beginning therapists frequently feel that there must be one way in which the statement was intended and that the therapist should ascertain which among the four possibilities is the accurate or correct one. It is more reasonable to assume that each statement the patient makes, and indeed every act of life, is the overdetermined product of the interaction of many factors, each of which has somehow contributed at this moment to produce an act of behavior.

A simple choice situation from daily living may serve as an example of overdetermination. If a pencil and a pen are placed alongside each other on the desk and the person seated there is in need of a writing implement his simple choice can itself be determined by many influences. Indeed, the motivations underlying the choice may be very complex. He might want to pick up the pen because it is customarily used in his work. He might prefer to pick up the pencil because just that morning his pen leaked and he was aggravated about it. He might tend to pick up the pen because of long training in school which indicated that the use of a pencil is in rather poor taste. A desire to choose the pencil might arise because of his generally compulsive manner and the need for frequent erasures. The selection might conceivably relate to early parental attitudes; perhaps there was hostility toward a father who wouldn't let his pen be used. Constitutional factors may contribute to his choice; his handedness may make grasping the right implement easier than grasping the left one. These factors, as well as many others may play a role in the final action.

The concept that multiple motivations or several significant aspects of personality find expression in a single behavior is crucial if one is to apply this system of analysis to therapy. By analyzing the patient's statement from a number of points of view, all having some possible explicatory usefulness, a therapist can greatly increase the number of options he has in formulating therapeutic responses.

THE CONTENT

The content may be described as the manifest meaning of the material the patient has presented: facts, opinions, conjectures, questions and so on. Most conversation deals with the content aspect of communication. In therapy, if the content of the patient's statement is clear, the content analysis will be simple and will consist of a summary with a rearrangement for clarity.

Examples

O: "I'm doing OK I guess. I'm not failing. I'm failing one subject —I might bring that up this time, I'm not sure. I'm doing good work, in it, uh . . . but I just dread getting it (my report card) because it's got to be perfect, you know. If it's not perfect you better watch out."

Summary for Content: I don't think I'm failing. There is one subject I'm worrying about. I work hard, but they want perfection.

R: "I keep saying he's going to be wonderful, he's going to be fine, everything is going to be fine. He (husband) keeps saying, 'I'm glad you think so.'"

Summary for Content: I say he'll be fine; my husband disagrees.

At times the content of a unit may be complex, ambiguous

or contradictory. When this is the case, the therapist is forced to wonder what dynamic, cognitive or transference problems have led to the patient's difficulty in expression or organization of content.

Examples

O: [discussing why his stepfather refused to accept money from his grandmother to make a down payment on the house] "I think it was just because he was mad at, uh at my mother 'cause she got mad because he's been going to these hockey games lately and she doesn't like him to go to the hockey games . . . which is probably right, she probably doesn't but nevertheless . . . either that or he's too proud to take the money from my grandmother."

Summary for Content: I guess it was because he is angry at my mother because she is angry at him or it may be because he is too proud to take money from grandmother. This contrast of possible reasons suggests that O is either too guilty or frightened to maintain this criticism very long or that his positive feelings about his stepfather are producing ambivalence.

R: "Well, like this afternoon, when he joined the Boys' Club (which he joined some months before) they went on a boat trip. I can understand his feeling too . . . but, ah, I guess underneath it is the fact that he was hit pretty hard that one day . . . and he said . . . the way he said it this morning that if it's four again, forget it."

Summary for Content: This statement was incomprehensible to the therapist. R is trying to explain why her son is so reluctant to come for his therapy hours, but the issue is so anxiety-provoking that she is unable to produce a clear statement. There are two probable sources of her anxiety. It may be a derivative of her guilt at participating in what she now views as an attack on her son or a consequence of her anger at the therapist for allowing and encouraging the discussion which upset the boy. It is, of course, possible that both factors play a part.

Therapy differs from other forms of verbal interaction and

human interaction in many ways. One of the most important of these differences occurs because the content or overt meaning of the patient's statement ceases to be the focus of the interaction, and comes to be seen primarily as a vehicle through which the patient's "underlying conflicts" become apparent. To the extent that this is true, focussing upon the overt or content meaning of the patient's remarks is non-therapeutic. It is difficult for the new therapist to avoid content remarks, however, because of all of the experience he has had in focussing upon content. (Parenthetically, when therapists choose to respond to other than content aspects of statements in ordinary social conversations, it appears to arouse considerable anxiety in others.) In general, responding to content is both the simplest and least therapeutic response which can be made.

THE AFFECT

The affect analysis assumes that the content of each patient unit has an accompanying component of affective expression. Indeed, there may be a whole complex of feelings which are expressed in a single statement. For our purposes, however, we usually are satisfied to describe the dominant feeling or the predominating cluster of feelings which underlies the material the patient produces. The analysis for affect frequently requires knowledge of the patient's tone of voice and the context in which the statement was made. The words themselves, in transcript, may convey very little feeling. The interpretations of many of the following statements will emphasize the necessity of having a knowledge of the patient's voice tone, style of delivery and context when attempting an analysis of affect.

Examples

O: "We decided two weeks ago that we were going to come every week, so this is the first time we get together."

Summary for Affect: The words themselves have a detached 'the best laid plans' quality which is contradicted by a number of other factors. The patient blurted out this statement as he entered the office, while therapist was closing the window against street sounds, and followed it with a fairly long discussion in which he denied any fault for this occurrence and displaced blame for therapist's inconvenience on his mother. O's anxiety over failing to honor his commitment to the therapist is more evident in his rush of speech and the subsequent choice of topic than in the words themselves.

R: "We're supposed, we're going away next week, we won't be here, we'll be out of town . . . so he took it in his head . . . you know I told him that, he was just terrible that week he wouldn't come—just impossible—so I said well be a good boy, we're going away regardless but I thought it would be a bribe . . . we'll go away for a few days . . . so he took it into his head that this'll—that he's only coming until we go away you know. . . ."

Summary for Affect: R did not announce her intention to cancel her next appointment in a clear fashion but instead gave the information while discussion of her son's behavior continued. Her fast speech, her hesitation and repetition, and her attempt to divert attention to her son all indicate the anxiety she feels about cancelling an appointment.

Subjective discomfort in the patient is most likely to result from the affect associated with the material being discussed. In responding to this discomfort, it is not sufficient to have decided that the patient is expressing a particular feeling; the therapist should also attempt to gauge the pervasiveness and depth of the feeling. That is, he should concern himself with the quantitative aspects of the affect expressed.

Examples

O: [Discussing grades] "I'm doing OK, I guess. I'm not failing. I'm failing on one subject—I might bring that up this time, I'm not sure. I'm doing good work, work in it, uh. But I just dread getting it (my report card) because it's got to be perfect, you know? If it's not perfect why you better watch out."

Summary for Affect: Here, while it is obvious that anxiety and some guilt over failing to meet standards are present, what appears to be crucial is the primitive nature of the feelings indicated by the words "dread" and the childlike statement, "you better watch out."

R: "'Cause he (husband) is, ah, you know, he's an introvert and God forbid anything happens to B. I think he would crack up completely—because he just adores him . . . he . . . as much as they've fought and everything, he just adores this child—and, ah,—I think he would just crack up—and he would probably blame me—'cause I want him to have a normal life. . . ."

Summary for Affect: R is extremely anxious and is frightened by her awareness that she was responsible for electing surgery in the face of her husband's opposition. The extent of anxiety is indicated by her invocation of the Deity, which is very atypical of her, and by her choice of such extreme phrases as "crack up completely" and "just adore."

It is frequently useful to assess the appropriateness of the feeling and, in those instances where it appears inappropriate, to seek for an understanding of the inappropriate reaction.

Examples

O: "We decided two weeks ago that we were going to come every week, so this is the first time we get together (pause) last week, week before last, I stayed out at my father's house all week that's why I wasn't in."

T: "Your mother called me."

O: "Kinda late, though, huh?" O proceeded to displace the blame for the week under discussion on to his mother.
[This example occurred in the middle of the series of statements concerning failure to keep appointments which is discussed on pages 80, 82 and 84.]

Summary for Affect: In this instance the patient's anxiety that he might be blamed was so great that he felt compelled to complete his ritual of excuses and displacement in spite of the therapist's willingness to accept his not having come. The therapist's acceptance of his acting out is insufficient to reduce the patient's anxiety or to end his defensive maneuvers.

R: "I know that, that it's (the operation) going to be more than fine (laugh). No, I feel bad, I'm sorry that he's (husband) going through that if he feels that strongly (that the boy will not survive surgery)—and you know if down deep he really feels that, that must be terrible for him."

Summary for Affect: The patient's laugh during this statement had a quality which was strikingly different from the previous tone and the somewhat softer tone which accompanied the "I feel bad." R is defiantly rejecting information about surgery because it threatens to release her anxiety perhaps by clarifying or underlining some of the reality bases for apprehension about the surgery. While a softer feeling emerges, she still refuses to acknowledge the validity of her husband's feelings with her words "if he feels" and "if down deep."

In order for the therapist to truly grasp the significance of his patient's communication, he must remain aware of the affective components of the patient's expression. One way to maintain heightened awareness of the patient's affective state is to try to feel as the patient does; to wonder repeatedly how one might feel in the particular situation provided one shared the patient's background. For the most part, however, the patient's typical affective reactions and his typical way of expressing them must be learned—learned by attentive listening and watching.

THE DYNAMICS

In this approach to therapy we assume first that the patient's personality is the result of an orderly series of events, which have been summarized in the dynamic formulation, and second that every statement which the patient makes in treatment has some relevance for understanding his life experiences. We may further assume that not only is there a relationship between the dynamic content of a statement and the patient's general dynamics but that specific problem areas are also involved. Frequently the interaction between a particular set of demands and the patient's dynamic structure will produce a problem which leads the patient to decide to enter treatment. This decision to enter therapy leads to great personal discomfort; it is usually inconvenient, expensive and painful for him to remain in therapy. Because of his motivation to reduce his discomfort, it is reasonable to assume that specific problem areas will be prominent in his productions, even if they are not as directly stated as the therapist might wish.

Examples

O: "I'm doing OK, I guess. I'm not failing. I'm failing in one subject. I might bring that up this time, I'm not sure. I'm doing good work, work in it, uh, but I just dread getting it, (my report card) because it's got to be perfect, you know. If it's not perfect, why, you better watch out."

Summary for Dynamics: Denial of the threatening knowledge that he is not doing adequate work is basic here. The patient must protect himself and avoid guilt feelings. His failure to do adequate work is intimately associated with and displaced upon his parents; the apprehension which underlies this blame-avoidance and the simultaneous anger at his parents are equally evident. With this patient the conjunction of blame avoidance, displacement and rage occurs over and over again.

R: "Oh yes, I put him (my son) in the closet—he cried—he sat there, then the next time, he had it all rigged up with a radio and he had all (laugh) he had feathered his nest (laugh) wrishhhh 'oh, sure glad to go in the closet'— (laughing) he didn't scream, didn't rave, didn't rant, he was all ready to go, in fact his brother had the closet fixed near him so they could talk to each other through the wall, so that's no good at all—"

Summary for Dynamics: R is unable to accept suggestions from persons who she perceives as authority figures, like her therapist, but is sufficiently dependent upon their approval that she cannot openly reject the suggestions. Instead, she allows or perhaps encourages behavior in others which will make the suggestion unworkable. The specific problem referred to (one of the presenting complaints) is her inability to control her son's behavior. The suggestion of closeting the son before things got out of hand was made after a series of events which seemed potentially very destructive; these included a serious and nearly successful attempt of the son to set the mother afire with charcoal lighter fluid and some altercation between the son and the building janitor which resulted in the police being called. Even in the face of such serious events, R is unable to make more than a gesture of attempting to control her son, probably because she fears that her own anger is unmanageable and that she will lose control. There is also some note of pride at his cleverness in evading the intent of her power assertion; one must therefore also consider the possibility that her failures to control her son result in part from the vicarious satisfaction which she derives from his open flouting of authority figures, even though she is one of the main figures so treated. Equally interesting is the relationship between punishment and control she is seeking. Permitting the child to listen to the radio in the closet might effectively keep him out of mischief. It is not acceptable to her, however, because it would not be punishment.

Sometimes the therapist will find that the dynamic content of a statement is not congruent with the dynamic formulation. When this is the case he is becoming aware of a new facet of the patient's functioning or correcting an impression which is no longer tenable. Such changes in the dynamic formulations are inevitable and highly desirable for one's knowledge of the patient should be growing and changing as treatment progresses.

Examples

O: "I guess she thought I was going to come in. I don't know. 'Cause she called me about 8:30, about 8:00 or so and said are you going. I said 'No, I told you.' There wasn't time to get from there to here and she says well (mumbles). I told her to call sooner, but she says that, uh, before when she called someone, I say that she shouldn't call so early. She shouldn't wait until the appointment's almost over to call. Other than that I don't know of anything unusual."

Summary for Dynamics: This statement was one of a series concerning O's apprehensions about failure to keep appointments and led to the following formulation: Frequently O shifts the problem of dealing with authority figures to others; this enables him to displace blame and anger onto them when things go wrong. This was one of the first opportunities to study in detail his techniques for avoiding blame and led to the realization that the more or less classic triangle of denial, displacement and avoidance was operating here, and that the anger discussed above occurred when these defenses were threatened.

R: "Oh, yes, I put him in the closet—he cried—he sat there, then the next time, he had it all rigged up with a radio he had all (laugh) he had feathered his nest (laugh) wrishhhhh, 'oh sure, glad to go in the closet'— (laughing) he didn't scream, didn't rave, didn't rant—he was all ready to go—in fact his brother had the closet fixed near him so he could go into his closet and they could talk to each other through the wall, so that's no good at all—"

Summary for Dynamics: While handling of her own dependency needs was noted as some problem in the dynamic formulation, it seemed that R ordinarily reacted to situations in which she held a dependent or receptive position by aggressive attack on the nurturing figure. For the first time, in this statement, evidence is presented which indicates that she does not always reject support or advice openly but manages through subtle uses of other's behavior to deny that the supporting figure is of any actual help to her. Having recognized this maneuver, it is easier to see the reason for her many failures in applying child control techniques which are successful for her mother, her sister and her friends. To her view, apparently, her failure does not point to her inadequacy or need for support but rather indicates that the supporting or advising figure would also experience failure in attempting to control her "impossible" son.

Frequently statements will appear to be too trivial to possess much dynamic content. It is desirable, however, to seek the dynamic significance of all statements rather than to assume that none is present without careful reflection.

Examples

O: " 'Cause she called me about 8:30, about 8:00 or so and said are you going. . ."

Summary for Dynamics: " 'Cause she called me about 8:30." The later mother calls the more irresponsible and blamable she is. "About 8:00 or so." This suggests the primitive, magical conception he has integrated of his mother, the implication is that she will somehow know that he has lied about her. The desire to avoid blame which leads to denial and displacement simultaneously limits the usefulness of displacement.

R: "Those paintings are beautiful–reminds me of things the boys used to do."

Summary for Dynamics: This statement came in the middle of a long pause in a discussion of marital difficulties. R was referring to fingerpaintings done by a child patient which were hanging in the therapist's office. While this appears to be a trivial comment on the environment, the therapist considers it to be an example of R's capacity to deny significance to or to avoid thinking about problems by orienting her perceptions around external, relatively neutral stimuli. In this instance, her apparent effort to avoid the problem under discussion was not successful since she ended the ensuing pause by reviving the previous recital of complaints against her husband.

The dynamic significance of a statement is always important, however recognizing it is not something which automatically occurs to new therapists because this is not the customary mode of comprehending communications. A therapist must train himself to enhance his awareness. As with so many aspects of psychotherapy, prolonged conscious consideration should lead to a more rapid awareness of the dynamic significance of the material as it is being presented.

THE TRANSFERENCE

We assume that every statement that a patient makes in therapy includes some implications about the therapist-patient relationship. The importance of psychotherapy to the patient has been emphasized; for the duration of treatment the therapist is an important individual in his patient's life.

Since knowledge about the patient's other relationships comes second-hand and is frequently subject to distortion, the therapeutic relationship provides the therapist's best opportunity to see the patient in reality. While many of the patient's distortions are patently obvious, or can be discerned from careful study of historical information, the patient's reaction patterns in the therapy situation bear considerable resemblance to his behavior in other situations; unquestionably, there are some unique features arising from the therapy situation; however, the patient cannot be something that he is not, and the bulk of the characteristics which he displays can be assumed to be deeply rooted in his personality.

Further, and most crucial, the therapeutic relationship gives the patient an opportunity for emotional and cognitive experiencing which provides the atmosphere for new growth. It is essential that the therapist understand this aspect of the interaction if he is to make maximum curative use of it.

The implications about the therapist-patient relationship which can be drawn from patient statements are divisible into two main types: those implications which reflect the effect of the therapist's personality on the patient and those which are relevant to the patient's perceptions about the therapist and the relationship. There are three aspects of the patient's perception of the therapist which can be at least logically distinguished.

These are the perception of the therapist as a person, as an authority figure and as a distortion of previous authority figures. We have subsumed all of these under the general term of transference, although this usage is obviously much broader than the definition given to transference by several theoretical groups. The first transference implication which can be considered is the manner in which the patient's statement reflects the effect of the therapist's personality.

Examples

O: "We decided two weeks ago that we were going to come every week, so this is the first time we get together."

Summary for Transference: The fact that this irregularity of treatment visits occurred is in part a function of this therapist's difficulties in dealing with failures and cancellations with adolescents because this problem relates to his functioning as an authority figure. Such a conceptualization and a simultaneous conviction that the patient will function best at his own pace can lead to the patient's being given more responsibility for arrangements than he can assume, especially relatively early in treatment. As was pointed out previously, there were many indications of anxiety surrounding this statement. The next statement was:

O: "Last week, week before last, I stayed out at my father's house all week, that's why I wasn't in . . ."

O's inability to conceptualize an authority figure as other than judgmental and puntive leads to his usual self-protective statement of "not guilty." Part of the anxiety he feels is undoubtedly generated by guilt over feelings that he might have kept his appointment. The therapist's failure to appreciate and deal with his anxiety over this issue led to the displacement of blame on to his mother which was noted in the previous example. Had the therapist been able to deal with the patient's anxiety here the displacement of blame discussed above might not have been necessary.

R: "Crazy, isn't it? Huh?"

Summary for Transference: This remark followed the pause which followed a long statement by the patient, which might well have been responded to by the therapist but was not. The therapist, insecure about competence and painfully aware of the tape recorder in the early hours with a new therapy patient, is likely to respond verbally quite infrequently. This places the patient in a situation where she must demand feedback. It is felt that the patient's almost manneristic use of the phrase, "you know," reflects the same problem. The patient is not sure that the therapist does understand what has been going on.

We are also interested in the perceptions and distortions about the therapist or the nature of the relationship which are introduced because the patient conceptualizes the therapist as he has others, particularly those who have been in positions of authority.

Examples

O: [in response to a statement by the therapist that he wasn't certain he understood something] "Well, it's—you know—like I said. I mean, I talked a lot about it."

Summary for Transference: Here it appears that O can only interpret the therapist's comment as criticism of him, and responds with confusion and then with blame avoidance. He seems to assume that there must be some blame when an authority figure is not able to understand or asks for clarification.

R: "I was telling Dr. F. (son's therapist) that B says this is the last time he is coming . . ."

Summary for Transference: R cannot tell the therapist directly but gives the information in her report of an already accomplished conversation. She knows that by prior agreement her treatment and the treatment of B are not mutually dependent and that she can continue whether or not he does. She also knows that the therapist believes that the son should continue. Even though her own treatment will not necessarily be affected, she assumes the offensive, taking the faintly dishonest tack of informing the therapist in a manner which deals with the problem as a *fait accompli.* This approach is very similar to her manner of dealing with her mother when she has or is about to condone behavior in her sons which her mother will strongly disapprove.

APPLICATION OF THE SYSTEM OF ANALYSIS

We have described the four vantage points from which every patient communication unit may be considered. While this is a very demanding and time consuming procedure the understandings obtained when one analyzes even a few statements from any given treatment hour justify the effort. It has been our practice to require that a beginning therapist apply the system of analysis to some portion of the recording of every treatment hour for which he is being supervised. It is best to select that portion of the hour in which there has been the most back and forth discussion. The written analysis can then be reviewed by the supervisor in as much detail as is desirable. Similar analyses have been prepared for use in peer group supervisory sessions and can provide the basis for therapy discussions.

Chapter VII

THE THERAPIST'S RESPONSE

THE THERAPIST'S JOB is to use himself to advance the patient's benefit and understanding; to use himself to communicate to the patient in a helping fashion. This task has three aspects to it—understanding the patient, comprehending his statements and responding in a fashion which leads to the achievement of proposed goals.

While it is true that communications are complex and multi-dimensional, that a great deal is communicated non-verbally and that the therapist should be aware of it, the fact remains that at present verbal responses are the therapist's basic tool and his skill at using them, his basic skill. Since the essence of the therapy hour is verbal, a record of the verbal exchanges which occurred during the hour is essential to the learning of psychotherapy. The only totally accurate, practical method of recording hours is on tape.

The use of the tape recorder is an anxiety-producing experience for most, perhaps for all new therapists. It is not necessarily anxiety-provoking for all patients. Whether the tape recorder is introduced at the beginning of treatment, or after a number of contacts; whether it is used consistently or intermittently, patients can respond to the tape recorder without anxiety when it is properly handled by the therapist. The total effect of taping is incalculable and varies from patient to patient. In some cases its effects are undoubtedly detrimental (as in patients with paranoid trends, for example) but in others it appears to be a positive experience for the patient. Often it is taken by the patient as a sign of caring on the part of the therapist. It seems very likely, however, that the patient's response to recording is, in most cases, a reflection of the therapist's response. If the therapist feels it is beneficial, it is likely that the patient will, also. If he feels it is threatening, the patient will feel threatened. Our insistence upon tape recording is not based upon the opinion that it is not as detrimental to therapy as is usually assumed, but upon the belief that it is the best possible method to learn to do psychotherapy.

After the tape is made, it must be studied. This study is useful at any time, but it is most productive if the dynamic formulation has been written, the goals have been determined and the therapist is concerned with understanding what the patient is saying; with trying to devise a means of approaching the goals of therapy, and with studying the patient's defenses. For this study, the therapist selects a recent therapy tape and begins playing it at the very beginning, analyzing it for the theme of the hour. When he is satisfied that he knows the theme he then proceeds through the hour, one unit at a time. Ideally he would analyze every communication unit of the hour. If this is impossible the hour should be randomly sampled and a few communication units studied; it is useful to analyze the discussion of a few single topics from beginning to end, rather than skipping about the tape analyzing small segments at many points.

To analyze a communication unit the therapist plays a complete statement by the patient and then turns off the tape recorder. He then interprets the patient's statement from each of the four points of view we have discussed previously (content, affect, dynamics, transference), in brief written form. Next, he creates and writes a response which he deems most effective in assisting the patient toward the goals. Following this, the actual response which was made during the hour is listened to, and classified into one of the categories to be defined in this chapter. The therapist then compares his actual response to the "most effective" response he has just created. This helps immeasurably in understanding the weaknesses in one's therapeutic responses.

The therapist then plays the next patient response, listening to hear the patient's reaction to the type of response he has just made. While this appears an extremely elaborate technique it is amazing how much solid information can be elicited from the analysis of even a few remarks. The outcome of so detailed an analysis is not only a better understanding of the patient but also a heightened awareness during the therapy hour.

The focus of this chapter will be the categorization of the therapist's responses. With few exceptions, all are potentially therapeutic, if wisely used. The extent to which a particular classification of remarks is considered to be therapeutic will depend on the prior experience, personal proclivities and the orientation of the therapist, the needs and current status of the patient, the goals which have been set out and other factors. It is generally incorrect and limiting to assume that there is but one response which is the "best" for each situation, or that it is always best to make a response. A good statement by one therapist would not necessarily be good if made by another therapist. A statement which is useful for one patient is not necessarily useful for another. There are probably no ultimate or perfect responses. There is, however, a criterion for the goodness of a therapist's response. The criterion is that the response be useful to the patient, useful in the sense that it brings the patient closer to a goal. We assume that the most useful response is one which discusses some aspect of a patient's behavior in terms of its relationship to a goal in a fashion which the patient understands.

If responses which appear useful to the therapist fail to lead the patient toward these goals (recognizing that progress may be slow), the therapist should reexamine the goals, examine the nature of the patient's resistance more carefully and concern himself with the accuracy of his formulation.

If a response does not appear useful, it is helpful to wonder why one responded in this particular manner. Can the therapist discern a trend in himself to respond inappropriately to a particular type of material or with a particular patient? Has he discovered an area where he might have unresolved conflicts himself? Is there a facet of the patient's dynamics which is not understood? Is there something about the patient-therapist relationship that requires more careful exploration? These are the sort of questions that we must have the courage to ask and answer, supported by the knowledge that areas of conflict are universal.

When first attempting this procedure, discouragement is inevitable. While listening to a recording one has the advantage of hindsight. There are no time limitations in considering a suitable response. Anxiety in the therapist is probably less than it was during the treatment hour. Such careful scrutiny of our therapeutic efforts is difficult and painful; however, a detailed review of therapy hours should result in improvement in the therapist's skill.

We turn now to the vehicle through which this increased skill will be displayed—the therapist's response. In order to simplify the task of giving examples of responses, and also to indicate the wide array of responses which are possible for almost any statement, we are employing the same statements throughout the chapter.

The statements used are as follows:

Patient R: "I was telling Dr. F that B says this is the last time he is coming—he just doesn't want to come any more and today I think he let out the reason—it isn't only about the boys' club—it's as if there's any more of these four people conferences, you know—that really reached him evidently—it made a big, big deep impression . . ."

Patient O: "Everything else is going fine—no trouble at all, I'm not arguing with my mother any more. (Pause) Nothing at all, I never even get excited."

Let us turn now to the delineation of the possible responses to these statements.

RESPONSE AT THE CONTENT LEVEL

This response is directed to the content aspect of the patient's statement. It is close to the level at which ordinary conversation is most frequently conducted, except that it frequently summarizes a more discursive patient statement.

Examples

R: "I was telling Dr. F. that B says this is the last time he is coming—he just doesn't want to come any more and today I think he let out the reason—it isn't only about the boys' club—it's as if there's any more of these four people conferences, you know—that really reached him evidently—it made a big, big deep impression . . ."

T: "He says he isn't coming any more—but you don't think missing the boys' club trips is the real reason that he wants to quit coming—"

O: "Everything else is going fine—no trouble at all, I'm not arguing with my mother any more. (Pause) Nothing at all, I never even get excited."

T: "Things have settled down, especially with your mother."

The best use of the content response is to encourage the patient to discuss some aspect of his previous statement. This is quite useful in eliciting information or giving permission to discuss certain problem areas. In making content responses or indeed any response, it is better to avoid structuring statements or questions in a manner which permits a simple one word response; ordinarily much richer statements are obtained by phrasing questions in a more general and open-ended manner.

Examples

R: "I was telling Dr. F. that B says this is the last time he is coming—he just doesn't want to come any more and today I think he let out the reason—it isn't only about the boys' club—it's as if there's any more of these four people conferences, you know—that really reached him evidently—it made a big, big deep impression . . ."

T: "You think it is more to avoid another conference than because he is missing boy's club trips?" (Likely to produce a single word response.)

T: "I wonder what it was about the conference that made such a big impression—that he doesn't want to come anymore . . ." (Requires a longer response.)

O: "Everything else is going fine—no trouble at all, I'm not arguing with my mother any more. (Pause) Nothing at all, I never even get excited."

T: "You think that this time things have settled down with your mother."
(This, of course, again enables the patient to simply reply yes.)

T: "That's interesting, why don't you tell me more about that?" (This is of course the classic leading response. One can, however, vary it somewhat to incorporate more specific content, for example, "I'm interested in your saying, 'I never get excited' —could you tell me a little more about that?")

It is easy to influence the reply to a question by suggesting that one answer is more acceptable than another by the words or the tone of voice. When this has occurred it may be very difficult to know whether the response is to be interpreted as an attempt to please the therapist or a valid statement of fact.

Examples

R: "I was telling Dr. F. that B says this is the last time he is coming—he just doesn't want to come any more and today I think he let out the reason—it isn't only about the boys' club—it's as if there's any more of these four people conferences, you know—that really reached him evidently—it made a big, big deep impression . . ."

T: "It doesn't seem to me that the conference was that upsetting. Don't you think that he is just looking for an excuse to quit seeing Dr. F?"

O: "Everything else is going fine—no trouble at all, I'm not arguing with my mother any more. (Pause) Nothing at all, I never even get excited."

T: "Aren't you sort of saying that a lot of the arguments are your fault?"

Many patients experience difficulty in dealing with "why?" questions. This is because "why" requests a response which explains motivation. Every act, no matter how simple, can be considered to be motivated in many ways. It may be difficult for the patient to discern the level at which he is expected to reply; it is also difficult to be aware of and to verbalize one's motivations when questioned thus, abruptly. A more desirable form might be "I wonder what considerations went into . . ." or, "could you tell me about some of your thoughts when you decided to . . ." A more directive form might be " could it be that part of the reason you . . . was because . . .?"

The content response then enables the therapist to focus the patient on certain aspects of his statement. As such it can be very useful; the great danger in responding specifically to content is that it can turn therapy into conversation.

THE SIMPLE CONTINUING RESPONSE

The simple continuing response includes all therapists' activities which are designed to promote a continuation of the patient's discussion without influencing the direction the discussion takes. This type of response is distinguished from the content response by virtue of the deliberate attempt to play no role other than to encourage the patient to continue talking. Many good therapists employ this type of response more than any other, but this approach can pose problems for the beginner, who feels the need to be therapeutic, wants to see rapid change and is concerned that his patient and his supervisor will develop a poor opinion of him. Often he attempts to overcome these problems by being more active than may really be desirable.

There are two purposes which the simple continuing response may serve. The first use is appropriate when one wishes to hear more about a subject without influencing the direction the patient takes. Once the therapist makes another type of response, the patient may be influenced in a manner which is difficult to determine. The second purpose occurs when the patient makes a totally unexpected statement which does not appear to fit into our prior understanding of this person. In this instance time is needed to think and to understand, rather than to blunder in while uncertain. A good general rule about psychotherapy is that when there is doubt about the proper therapeutic maneuver, it is best to obtain more information.

The amount of activity engaged in by the therapist in making continuing responses can be conceptualized as occupying a continuum. At one end of the continuum absolutely nothing is done. The patient completes his statement and the therapist merely waits motionless for him to continue. Time lapses usually work favorably for the therapist; the patient generally feels pressure to fill the void and usually does so; the beginning therapist also feels this pressure and unfortunately, often cannot resist it. The next step along the continuum might be merely an expectant look, possibly with raised eyebrows. Leaning forward in an expectant manner or, if notes are being taken, holding the pencil poised in writing position tends toward the more active end of the continuum. Vocal production of various sorts also lie in this region on the continuum. The simplest is a grunt or a little noise of any sort. A simple "uh-huh" or what may be described as an expectant "yes" are helpful. The technique which is most likely to work, although it does involve emphasizing part of what the patient has said and hence may mildly influence his direction is that of repeating the last few words or phrases of the patient's statement with a question mark at the end of it. A simple request to hear more about the same subject is often effective; this is probably about as active a simple continuing response as might be expected.

Beginners frequently feel that techniques such as these designed to encourage the patient to talk, are not quite cricket. They feel that the verbal production should be natural, that the patient will become aware of the process and will believe that it is "gimmicky." The verbal tools a therapist develops are his stock in trade and skillful application of a variety of techniques is not only permissible but mandatory. Patients rarely seem to be disturbed by these methods, and usually correctly perceive these behaviors as cues that the therapist wants him to continue. In many respects they are like the techniques that many "good listeners" employ in conversation.

On occasion the beginner will become discouraged with the application of this category of responses because they do not work well for him. He knows that they work well for others but this information hurts rather than helps for secretly he feels inept and deficient. When this occurs it discourages continued use of the response. It is easier for the beginner if he understands that these techniques, although simple on the surface, are in fact quite difficult and require practice and conscious thought for proficiency. The early period of deliberate planning and practice is difficult but eventually there is incorporation of the technique into his own functioning which produces a smoothness and naturalness that is quite gratifying.

In summary, the simple continuing response serves to encourage the patient to continue in the direction of his choice. It should be employed frequently. The beginner will have some difficulty in the initial application but should not allow himself to become discouraged.

RESPONSE AT THE AFFECT LEVEL

This response is one in which the therapist is attempting to respond to the patient's expressed affect. The range of possibilities encompasses any emotion that the human being is capable of experiencing. The ability to assess the feeling a patient experiences will vary with respect to different situations and different patients. Feelings may be extremely complex, difficult to unravel and difficult to communicate. In spite of this, this response is extremely valuable in making the patient feel understood and valued.

There are three general purposes behind the use of the affective response. The first is that of giving the patient permission to experience or express a particular feeling, especially feelings which may be culturally unacceptable. During the process of therapy the patient learns what is permissible in the therapeutic situation from cues the therapist provides. If he learns that expressions of hostility or sexual feelings or any other affect are unacceptable he is less likely to express them. If the therapist verbally expresses understanding of the existence of a feeling, and does so in an accepting manner, the patient will feel more freedom to explore this aspect of his functioning.

Examples

R: "I was telling Dr. F. that B says this is the last time he is coming—he just doesn't want to come any more and today I think he let out the reason—it isn't only about the Boy's Club—it's as if there's any more of these four people conferences, you know—that really reached him evidently—it made a big, big deep impression . . ."

T: "I wonder if you aren't feeling a little guilty about your part in that conference."

O: "Everything else is going fine—no trouble at all, I'm not arguing with my mother any more. (Pause) Nothing at all, I never even get excited."

T: "It feels good not to argue with your mother. I wonder if it's possible that it scares you to argue with her."

A second purpose for the affect response is that of helping the patient become aware of his own feelings. Difficulty in recognizing one's own affect is quite common and may be a source of difficulty in interpersonal relations. The problem may occur as a result of repression or simply a lack of having carefully considered the relationship between the affect and the situation. Finally, one can express understanding and empathy through the use of affect responses. In order to do this effectively one must somehow be able to experience something of what the patient is experiencing. This is accomplished by continuously striving to wonder how someone, and more particularly this person, might feel when faced with this set of circumstances. There is some danger that such conscious striving for empathy will become an intellectual exercise and that the replies will be sterile and ineffective; empathic responses should involve a high degree of emotional exchange. Making such responses on a purely intellectual level should be avoided.

Examples

R: "I was telling Dr. F. that B says this is the last time he is coming—he just doesn't want to come any more and today I think he let out the reason—it isn't only about the Boy's Club—it's as if there's any more of these four people conferences, you know—that really reached him evidently—it made a big, big deep impression . . ."

T: "You feel pretty sorry about that conference—pretty sorry that you helped to make a big deep impression and hurt B."

O: "Everything else is going fine—no trouble at all, I'm not arguing with my mother any more. (Pause) Nothing at all, I never even get excited."

T: "It just feels **good** not to be arguing with her . . ."

When a good deal of congruence with the patient is achieved by expressing the exact shade of feeling he is experiencing, and there is a real bond of exchange, the patient will sometimes cry, particularly if the affect is a negative one; explosions of anger and smiles of pleasure also occur after a meaningful response. In any event, the fact that this exchange has taken place will be obvious to the therapist; there develops a kind of glow and a feeling of certainty about the appropriateness of the communication.

If the therapist's certainty is a consistently poor predictor of the patient's response, his feelings about the area of exploration and about the patient might well be examined. In this situation the assumption is frequently made that the patient's lack of response constitutes denial. While the assumption may be valid, it may also be a rationalization to cover the therapist's inadequacies. If the patient is in fact denying a feeling and the assumption is correct, the possibility still exists that one's communications of the affective state are clouded or obscure.

In Rogerian or client-centered therapy this affect response is employed almost exclusively. A great deal of experimental work has been done with this method, and a good deal of theoretical description of the rationale behind its use and the technique of employing it are available (see Chapter XI).

We have seen, then, that the feeling response may be employed to grant permission for the expression of certain affects, to help create an awareness of existing feelings and as a means of communicating emotionally with the patient.

RESPONSE TO DYNAMICS

The dynamic response or interpretation is a statement which endeavors to explain some aspect of a patient's functioning in the light of his past experiences. The purposes to be achieved through use of the dynamic response include the resolution of conflict, the development of insight into the undesirable role that some aspect of the past is currently playing, the delineation of defenses, and the clarification of resistances.

Examples

R: "I was telling Dr. F. that B says this is the last time he is coming—he just doesn't want to come any more and today I think he let out the reason—it isn't only about the Boy's Club—it's as if there's any more of these four people conferences, you know—that really reached him evidently—it made a big, big deep impression . . ."

T: "I wonder if your concern about the impression that this has made on B isn't a reflection of your old concern that somehow you damaged him or made an impression on him before he was born."

O: "Everything else is going fine—no trouble at all, I'm not arguing with my mother any more. (Pause) Nothing at all, I never even get excited."

T: "I wonder if not arguing with your mother means she won't send you away."

Generally we conceive of dynamic responses as dealing with material that the patient is unaware of and with material which has relationships he does not perceive. There are essentially two classes of material for which the patient has no awareness. The first is repressed material. In the traditional Freudian paradigm one represses an affect or a wish which is associated with unacceptable consequences. In this model the emotional charge is the cause of the repression. Implicitly one assumes that the material was once conscious but has been repressed to avoid the painful affect associated with it. A second class of material which produces problems and is out of the patient's awareness consists of patterns of behavior which have developed as the consequence of maladaptive learning.

If the maladaptive learning occurred early or was traumatic one often refers to the behavioral consequences as a character disorder. Dynamic interpretations have been increasingly applied in an effort to reverse or correct such disorders. The patient may be unaware or only dimly aware of his tendencies to act in a given fashion, and when informed of them may feel guilty or ashamed and react defensively. It is frequently assumed that the patient is aware of the effect of his actions "on some level" but this may not be true of those character traits which arise from maladaptive learning. One cannot assume that the affects present during the original conditioning are involved at the time the interpretation is made.

When we make a dynamic interpretation, we are embarking into a painful area for the patient, and usually we are pointing out meanings the patient will not face. Often these interpretations arouse the patient's defenses. For this reason it is best to make dynamic interpretations in a tentative way, at least early in therapy. This enables the patient to reject the interpretation gracefully without believing that he will upset the therapist or elicit rejection.

Examples

R: "I was telling Dr. F. that B says this is the last time he is coming—he just doesn't want to come any more and today I think he let out the reason—it isn't only about the Boy's Club—it's as if there's any more of these four people conferences, you know—that really reached him evidently—it made a big, big deep impression . . ."

T: "I wonder—do you suppose you told Dr. F. first and then tell me because you feel men are more understanding than women."

O: "Everything else is going fine—no trouble at all, I'm not arguing with my mother any more. (Pause) Nothing at all, I never even get excited."

T: "I wonder if you sometimes argue with your mother because you think she doesn't love you."

The success of dynamic interpretations will depend upon a number of factors. Among these will be the accuracy of the interpretation, the manner in which it is presented and the relative size of the gap between the patient's current insights and the newly interpreted material. The accuracy depends upon our willingness and ability to know the patient well and to develop a real dynamic formulation which is constantly modified on the basis of newly acquired information. The manner of presentation of an interpretation is crucial. The therapist should not be accusatory (a very common error). He should not be so enamored of his own remarks that he is unable to accept the patient's rejection of them. Compassion and understanding for the patient and a humble knowledge that even therapists err (and repress) will help to lessen the sting when the patient appears to refuse to understand.

Examples

R: "I was telling Dr. F. that B says this is the last time he is coming—he just doesn't want to come any more and today I think he let out the reason—it isn't only about the Boy's Club—it's as if there's any more of these four people conferences, you know—that really reached him evidently—it made a big, big deep impression . . ."

T: "I am quite sure that you went to Dr. F. first in the same way that you used to run to your father first when you had to tell your mother something unpleasant." (Errors of accusation and lack of humility.)

O: "Everything else is going fine—no trouble at all, I'm not arguing with my mother any more. (Pause) Nothing at all, I never even get excited."

T: "I have the very strong feeling that you're letting things settle down to keep from looking at your relationship with your mother. I wonder if you're not also saying you'd like to end therapy." (Error of accusation, punishing a given kind of response and threatening withdrawal of the relationship as punishment.)

The distance between the patient's knowledge and the therapist's interpretation is a crucial consideration. The ability to deal with unconscious material varies in patients. In any patient there is a limited range of movement possible at any particular time. If the therapist tries to cover too much distance between the current level of insight and the interpretation, the patient will respond with resistance or with a genuine lack of comprehension.

Examples

R: "I was telling Dr. F. that B says this is the last time he is coming—he just doesn't want to come any more and today I think he let out the reason—it isn't only about the Boy's Club—it's as if there's any more of these four people conferences, you know—that really reached him evidently—it made a big, big deep impression . . ."

T: "I wonder if your concern about that conference doesn't come from your feelings about really expressing anger at B . . . remember, you used to worry that you might really hurt him when you were angry." (Relatively small step for this patient)

O: "Everything else is going fine—no trouble at all, I'm not arguing with my mother any more. (Pause) Nothing at all, I never even get excited."

T: "I wonder if you're not telling me this to please me." (An interpretation which this patient could not admit.)

Of course one assumes too much if he believes that the patient's behavior in therapy is an exact replica of behavior in other relationships. The treatment situation is unique and calls forth somewhat unique functioning. For example, many patients will hesitate to discuss positive aspects of their existence during the therapy hour, believing that this may be inappropriate.

RESPONSE AT THE TRANSFERENCE LEVEL

A common error of beginners involves minimizing the importance of the therapeutic relationship. Involving oneself in psychotherapy amounts to asking for help with those things that are most intimate and painful. One of the factors which permits the patient to continue is his relationship with the therapist. In active therapy the relationship is always very important; this is true even when it appears least likely. However, it is frequently necessary for both the patient and the new therapist to deny this. This mechanism serves to avoid the threat of being vulnerable. The new therapist will tend to minimize the importance of the relationship because he feels that little is going on and thus assumes that the patient doesn't value him. Since the therapist is involved in pointing out an important aspect of the patient's immediate behavior, transference statements generally arouse a good deal of anxiety in the patient. It is easy to see why the patient might interpret this as a form of rejection by the therapist. While it is best not to make transference interpretations until one is certain that the relationship will bear them, the danger with beginning therapists is that they will not make transference interpretations at all. The transference aspects of communications are the most subtle and the most difficult to respond to. It is also true that the patient will be less disturbed by transference interpretations when he has been confronted by a number of them. If the transference situation appears to be negative and such that therapy is likely to be terminated, it will have to be dealt with very quickly.

Transference interpretations serve one of two purposes: to provide the patient with information concerning his current behavior, and to provide information concerning other relationships. One of the frequent secondary problems created by emotional disturbances is the shutting off of the usual channels whereby the patient obtains positive information about his behavior. By positive we mean information which is relatively non-hostile, which bears some relationship to the person's needs and which is presented in an atmosphere in which the patient might accept it. The absence of adequate information prevents the patient from ever having a real appreciation of the type of impression that he makes with other people. This information is necessary if change is to occur. We can experimentally demonstrate that, unless the effectiveness of a particular behavior can be judged, learning may not take place; repeated trials alone do not necessarily lead to learning. The therapist is in a unique position to indicate the consequences of the patient's behavior in the manner which is most likely to prove acceptable to the patient.

Examples

R: "I was telling Dr. F. that B says this is the last time he is coming—he just doesn't want to come any more and today I think he let out the reason—it isn't only about the Boys' Club—it's as if there's any more of these four people conferences, you know—that really reached him evidently—it made a big, big deep impression . . ."

T: "I get the feeling that you would like to influence me to promise that there won't be any more four people conferences—so you won't have to struggle so hard with B to make him come."

O: "Everything else is going fine—no trouble at all, I'm not arguing with my mother any more. (Pause) Nothing at all, I never even get excited."

T: "I wonder if you don't tell me this hoping I'll say that you don't have to come any more."

There are always elements of the transference which replicate other important relationships. For this reason, the transference serves as an example of other relationships; what is learned in the therapy situation may be applied elsewhere. Through the transference interpretations the patient comes to understand the manner in which he distorts interpersonal relationships.

Examples

R: "I was telling Dr. F. that B says this is the last time he is coming—he just doesn't want to come any more and today I think he let out the reason—it isn't only about the Boys' Club—it's as if there's any more of these four people conferences, you know—that really reached him evidently—it made a big, big deep impression . . ."

T: "I wonder if you aren't hoping I'll assume some of the responsibility for the conference, so you won't have to feel quite so guilty about it."

O: "Everything else is going fine—no trouble at all, I'm not arguing with my mother any more. (Pause) Nothing at all, I never even get excited."

T: "You know I think it's very important to you to try to make adults fond of you."

The transference response may use either the patient or the therapist as the subject. From time to time the therapist may report his emotional response to the patient in general or, more commonly, to a specific situation. In doing this, good judgment must be employed. The therapist-patient relationship must be maintained in an intact manner; if one becomes too involved in discussing one's own feelings there may be an unintentional reversal of role with the patient becoming the therapist.

Examples

R: "I was telling Dr. F. that B says this is the last time he is coming—he just doesn't want to come any more and today I think he let out the reason—it isn't only about the Boys' Club—

it's as if there's any more of these four people conferences, you know—that really reached him evidently—it made a big, big deep impression . . ."

T: "I get the feeling you want me to feel guilty about that."

O: "Everything else is going fine—no trouble at all, I'm not arguing with my mother any more. (Pause) Nothing at all, I never even get excited."

T: "You know when you say that I kind of get the feeling you're trying to kid me."

More commonly the transference remark relates directly to the patient and to his activity toward the therapist without discussing the affect that has been aroused by this action.

Transference responses, then, provide the patient with information about his behavior and serve as an example of other relationships. Occasionally these responses include mention of an affective reaction on the part of the therapist but more commonly deal only with the patient.

THE DIRECTIVE RESPONSE

In this category we group advice, reassurance and suggestion. These terms are employed in the ordinary sense and do not require definition. Generally, the type of therapy that employs this category of responses exclusively may be thought of as less reconstructive and more oriented toward current functioning. However, the reconstructive and directive approaches are not mutually exclusive either with the same patient or even within the same hour.

The directive response is employed in several ways. It may be effective in providing strength when the patient is unable to function without external support. It may be possible to use a directive response to prevent a predictable and undesirable occurrence toward which a patient is heading. Finally this type of response may also serve as a means of communicating concern for the patient's welfare.

Examples

R: "I was telling Dr. F. that B says this is the last time he is coming—he just doesn't want to come any more and today I think he let out the reason—it isn't only about the Boys' Club—it's as if there's any more of these four people conferences, you know—that really reached him evidently—it made a big, big deep impression . . ."

T: "I'm sure it did make a big impression on B but he'll get over it—I don't think you have to worry about it."

O: "Everything else is going fine—no trouble at all, I'm not arguing with my mother any more. (Pause) Nothing at all, I never even get excited."

T: "I'm a little concerned that if you begin to have trouble again you will think it's your fault. I think you should realize that part of this is because your mother's probably calmed down, too."

When a person approaches a friend or relative about a problem he is likely to elicit a response which would be classified in this category. Frequently this is helpful. All of us have both given and received advice on many occasions.

This technique appears deceptively simple. A person is doing something which he shouldn't. Why not just tell him to stop? It has worked in everyday life. Why not here? The answer to the question is straightforward. The patient is likely to have received all sorts of advice, suggestions and reassurance before entering therapy. He has come to the professional because these techniques have failed in his outside life. His needs are greater and not satisfactorily dealt with in this manner.

In general, one might think that the therapeutic application of these techniques is not difficult; they therefore have a distinct appeal for the beginner. They are, however, very difficult to employ effectively, in the sense of producing real accomplishment. In general a therapist must be rather expert to employ directive responses and the beginner should avoid these approaches unless there has been a good deal of planning and careful consideration of the therapeutic desirability of the particular move. Many patients will create a sort of tantalizing vacuum in which the necessary advice seems to be so obvious that the therapist can barely restrain himself. This may be a trap in which the therapist is being manipulated into saying something that he will regret later. When the therapist becomes aware of this manipulation, he can, of course, interpret it on a transference level.

THE INTERRUPTING RESPONSE

It is usually advisable to allow the patient to complete a statement before replying. When the patient is concentrating on expressing his own thought, the therapist's statement will have much less impact and may not obtain the careful consideration it would otherwise deserve.

Examples

R: "I was telling Dr. F. that B says this is the last time he is coming—he just doesn't want to come any more and today I think he let out the reason—it isn't only about the Boys' Club—it's as if there's any more of these four people conferences, you know—that really reached him evidently—it made a big, big deep impression . . ."

T: (Interrupting) "Did you talk to Dr. F. earlier today?"

O: "Everything else is going fine—no trouble at all, I'm not arguing with my mother any more. (Pause) Nothing at all, I never even get excited."

T: "These things you've been talking about seem like your only real problems."

Overzealousness is the most frequent reason for interruption. The therapist becomes enamored of a remark he is contemplating and cannot wait to express it; this tendency is usually best suppressed. There are, however, occasions when interruption is desirable. Some patients employ constant talking defensively, and tend to prevent the therapist from becoming involved by the sheer volume of their vocal productions. In such instances it is desirable to interrupt. It is unwise, however, to assume that this is the case in the first few hours, because there often will be an accumulation of material which comes pouring out in a torrent early in therapy; this should be allowed to occur.

Interruption is also frequently necessary with very disturbed individuals. In this situation the therapist interrupts to provide reality testing. If allowed to ramble on unchecked the patient may become more and more confused and disorganized.

Granting these exceptions, interruptions should occur rather infrequently. A good general rule with respect to interruption is to avoid being impulsive. When an interruption is planned it is preferable to interrupt in two stages. The first stage is the actual interruption. The desire to make a communication is indicated. A pause follows which lasts until the patient's set is interrupted, after which the therapist makes his point. It is important to separate the interruption from the subsequent communication so that the patient will have an opportunity to adjust his attention from his own thoughts to the therapist's remarks.

Examples

R: "I was telling Dr. F. that B says this is the last time he is coming—he just doesn't want to come any more and today I think he let out the reason—it isn't only about the Boys' Club—it's as if there's any more of these four people conferences, you know—that really reached him evidently—it made a big, big deep impression . . ."

T: "Mrs. R; I'd like to comment at this point. (Pause) I wonder why you felt it was necessary to discuss this with Dr. F. first. Perhaps you wanted to set the stage for B's hour with him."

O: "Everything else is going fine—no trouble at all, I'm not arguing with my mother any more. (Pause) Nothing at all, I never even get excited."

T: "Let me think about that a minute. (Pause) You're saying something kind of important and good has happened at home."

THE INATTENTION RESPONSE

Therapists are human beings. Occasionally they will get caught up in their own reverie. A remark the patient makes sets off fantasies; a personal problem crowds into one's thoughts and one loses track of the hour. When he finds himself drifting the therapist may simply blurt out something. The usual cause of the inattention response is the therapist. If the patient is truly boring, one can approach this as a personality characteristic or a defensive operation which needs to be dealt with as does any other problem area.

Examples

R: "I was telling Dr. F. that B says this is the last time he is coming—he just doesn't want to come any more and today I think he let out the reason—it isn't only about the Boy's Club—it's as if there's any more of these four people conferences, you know—that really reached him evidently—it made a big, big deep impression . . ."

T: "Excuse me, I was wondering if the tape recorder is working right and I guess I didn't really hear what you said."

O: "Everything else is going fine—no trouble at all, I'm not arguing with my mother any more. (Pause) Nothing at all, I never even get excited."

T: "That's very good, I'm glad to hear that."

The therapist's spontaneous reaction to his sudden awareness that he has been day dreaming is usually not helpful. If the therapist then becomes embarrassed and anxious he may respond with a remark which is influenced by an unrepresentative fragment of what the patient has been saying. The comment will frequently be inappropriate, or one which is a product of his fantasies rather than the patient's. Even in this situation one must pause and exercise due deliberation before replying. It is important not to cover this error by lying. One may always apologize for losing track of the conversation. Very frequent episodes of inattention should lead to careful consideration of the entire therapeutic process focusing on the possible factors that seem to be producing the therapist's inability to attend to his patient. Is the inattention in relation to certain areas? With certain types of patients?

THERAPIST'S PROBLEM RESPONSE

Each of us has areas of unresolved conflict. Certain patients will arouse these conflicts, thus introducing difficulties into the therapeutic situation. If the conflicts are severe enough, effective therapy may not be possible. Unfortunately, there are no clear rules for determining when this is the case. Since conflict areas are universal the problem is a quantitative one and must be judged independently by each therapist for each of his patients or for the specific problems of each of his patients. This is the most difficult area in which to attempt to judge ourselves. Over a period of time the introspective therapist should learn the types of problems that he is unable to adequately master. Individual supervision during training should help to delineate these areas. When conflicts are intrusive in the therapy process, either certain patients or patients with certain problems will have to be avoided or the therapist will himself need therapy, depending upon the extent of his difficulties.

INTERPERSONAL ASSESSMENT OF THE THERAPIST'S RESPONSE

Up to this point, we have been concerned with evaluating the therapist's response. Now we complete the cycle and return to the patient as a source of information as to the usefulness of the statements made. Therapy is a dialogue, and as such is a two person system in flux. Eventually then one must look at the patient for evidence concerning the effectiveness of one's efforts. In doing this, however, we encounter a logical and operational discontinuity. Ultimately, the purpose of psychotherapy is to alter the patient's behaviors and feelings outside the therapy hour by what happens during the therapy. Unfortunately we rarely have real data concerning the patient's behaviors outside the hour, and hence can rarely judge the effectiveness of a particular piece of therapeutic effort against this criteria except as seen through the patient's eyes. It is possible, however, to test the effect of a remark by examining the patient's next statement. It is true that patients frequently mull over the contents of the hour long afterward and that a therapeutic statement may exert its effect after a considerable interval of time has elapsed. Further, judging the delayed efforts of a particular remark also depends on the patient's informing us directly or indirectly. The patient's immediate response to a statement is an important piece of information, and lends itself to the following analysis.

A patient can respond to a therapist's interpretive statements (usually affect, dynamic or transference) in one of five ways, each of which may have several meanings: (1) he may not respond at all; (2) he may ignore the remark and discuss an unrelated subject; (3) he may answer as though a different interpretation had been made; (4) he may deny the interpretation, or (5) he may accept the interpretation. We will discuss each of these in turn.

1. The meaning of the patient's failure to respond at all can be determined only on the basis of the nonverbal behavior. The patient might be silently considering the soundness of the interpretation in the light of his knowledge of himself. At the other extreme, the silence may be a hostile response to the interpretation. At times the import of the silence will be obvious; when it is not, an interpretation directed at its meaning may clarify the situation. In any event, the silence will end at some point, and the patient must then say something. What he then says can be interpreted in one of the following ways.

2. The patient may ignore the interpretation and continue pursuing a thought of his own. That is, he may avoid dealing directly with it. While this may occur because he was so preoccupied that he genuinely did not hear the remark, this is relatively infrequent. A much more likely possibility is that the

interpretation proved to be so difficult that it was immediately repressed or distorted.

Sometimes, one will note a change in the affect even though the words continue in the same vein. In any case if a patient proceeds as if the interpretation had not been made one should assume that in terms of the patient's current defensive structure, he is simply not ready to accept the interpretation.

3. At times the patient will respond in a manner which implies that the therapist made a remark other than the one he did. This sometimes occurs because of ambiguity in the therapist's phrasing. This can be checked by reviewing the statement. More frequently this behavior represents denial, projection, or aggression on the part of the patient. Such a response is difficult to handle. If the patient's statement is allowed to go unchallenged, it is as though the therapist tacitly agrees. On the other hand, if attempts are made to correct the distortion, the therapist tends to be placed on the defensive. Perhaps the best procedure is to wonder with the patient why he misinterpreted without going into details of the distortion.

4. At times a patient will deny an interpretation in a vigorous, vehement manner with much affect. This usually means that the patient was taken unawares, that the interpretation is quite relevant and that the upset is a result of insufficient time to incorporate the new information. The patient may also deny an interpretation with characteristic defensive maneuvers; some persons respond this way to anything new. It is not possible to know precisely what this means for it may be either a response to the unfamiliar or a response to the specific content of the interpretation.

Avoidance of the interpretation, vehement denial and characteristic denial are in many respects identical maneuvers which serve to give the patient a means of disavowing an interpretation. One is tempted to hypothesize a continuum in which the least upsetting interpretations are simply avoided, while extremely upsetting ones are vehemently denied. However, it is not this simple and it appears likely that these may be, in large part, characteristic interpersonal techniques relating as much to the patient's general dynamics as to the particular content involved.

The most meaningful approach would appear to be to note the patient's characteristic maneuvers and his deviations from them. The two types of responses discussed immediately above, avoidance and denial, are indications of the patient's having been unable to accept the therapist's interpretation. This does not mean that the response has been useless, however. The idea that there is an ideal time for a response is prominent in the field, and that if it is made at this time it will be immediately accepted. By inference then, the ideal would appear to be to judge the patient's mental state so well that one need make a response only once. It is also often implied that each inappropriate response adds to the patient's defensiveness. This *may* be correct if one considers a specific highly charged area. On the other hand, discussion by the therapist of areas that are generally highly threatening may serve gradually to enable the patient to reduce his anxiety, and more readily approach certain classes of feelings. In this framework a response would be judged as part of a strategy of responding to a certain area rather than as a single unit.

These classes of responses on the patient's part then refer to the rejection of an interpretation. In the next classes the patient does not express clear acceptance nor clear rejection. The first of these is denial, in which the patient appears to consider the therapist's response and then decides it is inaccurate. At times he will make a different, more accurate interpretation. In this situation, the therapist has little choice but to judge the substituted interpretation against his knowledge of the patient's dynamics, and the overall level of insight the patient has. With new therapists, the greater danger lies in the rejection of accurate insights by the patient rather than overenthusiastic acceptance of them.

5. The most difficult patient response to deal with occurs when the patient accepts the interpretation verbally, but only on an intellectual level, conveying an impression that very little impact has been made. The impression is strengthened by the absence of the expected affect and a lack of genuine "feel" to the patient's response.

On the other hand, a patient's reaction to a real insight, once observed, rings true and is not often mistaken. The purpose of an interpretation is, of course, to produce knowledge or insight in the patient. One is attempting to help the patient to realize that, without being aware of it he tends to use characteristic interpersonal maneuvers, or security operations, to hold certain beliefs, to have certain effects on others, to have certain feelings. In any case one is attempting to lead the patient to knowledge which he fears.

From this point of view it is not surprising that interpretive responses are rarely accepted, rather, it is surprising that they are ever accepted at all. When the therapist has understood the patient and communicated this understanding in a fashion the patient can accept, the patient's reaction should be roughly equivalent to the insight received. He may respond with anger or relief or anxiety, but he should respond in an affective manner which is proportional to the insight he has received; when this occurs the interpretation has been successful.

The purpose of an interpretation is to produce insight, and its effectiveness is judged according to the insight it produces. Other classes of response have other purposes and are judged according to their success in producing their aim. For example, many content responses are questions. A good question is one that leads to an answer with some detail and elaboration. Other content responses should lead to a flow of conversation. The simple continuing response is designed to encourage the patient to continue talking and its effectiveness is therefore easy to judge. Directive responses, if positively received, will usually produce acceptance, or a "think it over" reply. On the other hand the patient may produce reasons why this advise is not going to work or why this reassurance ignores the depth of the problem. The latter reaction tends to be indicative of failure of the response. One may also judge directive responses quite objectively by subsequently noting whether the advise or suggestion is followed. Similarly, the purposeful interruption is judged primarily by whether or not the patient is able to shift gears and tune in on the therapist's statement.

While the analysis of single statements can provide much

valuable information, it would seem that the analysis of sequences of statements might be even more enlightening. No therapist will accomplish his goals by making the single perfect response. It is only by building up a global experience both within and across treatment hours that the therapist can assist his patient in moving toward goals. Careful attention to the sequence of events should provide the therapist with an awareness of the flow of the therapy or of his own contribution to turbulence unconducive to a smooth flow.

SUMMARY

The therapist's response is the main vehicle by which he applies his expertness in helping his patient. It is important to distinguish therapy from ordinary conversation. Therapy must involve real emotional involvement on the part of the therapist; at the same time he must carefully consider and perhaps consciously plan his moves. In the beginning these requirements will appear to be mutually exclusive, for it is difficult to be natural and involved and yet consider each move carefully. Ultimately the techniques become completely incorporated into functioning and require little conscious consideration. During the long interim period, the gap is bridged by frequently revising the dynamic formulation and goals and by repeatedly reviewing the therapy tapes.

Chapter VIII

NON-VERBAL COMMUNICATION IN THE THERAPY HOUR

IN PSYCHOTHERAPY the primary form of communication is verbal. Therapy, however, does not occur as an interchange between two disembodied voices; rather, there are two living people together in a room, affecting each other in a multiplicity of ways —moving, gesturing, smiling, leaning forward, separating, smoking and even scratching. Quite often, indeed usually, the persons involved are only dimly aware of their behavior, or lack of it. In this chapter we will discuss these aspects of therapy. The term non-verbal communication was chosen to emphasize the idea that we are interested in the overall impressions conveyed by the persons involved.

To attempt to investigate non-verbal behavior in a manner analagous to our approach to verbal behavior would require sound movie techniques which are neither available nor practical. However, non-verbal behavior can be an important and sometimes crucial aspect of therapy. For this reason a discussion seems worthwhile even if it consists of only a few orienting remarks and perhaps the vague outline of a point of view.

We will assume from the outset that an individual's nonverbal behavior is related, in a highly complex fashion, to his own dynamic history, affective state and feelings about the therapist and that such gross behaviors as posture, gait and total bearing may derive from experiences which began even prior to his capacity for verbal expression. Similarly, the impact of his overall bodily behavior on himself and on others may relate in part to the earliest levels of experience. We are a long way from being able to conceptualize the meaning of many of these factors, except perhaps in the grossest and simplest terms.

Non-verbal communication can be examined from several vantage points: a person's global interpersonal effect; his social role communications and those behaviors which are apparently designed to elicit action from the therapist. Other aspects of non-verbal communication concern subtle motor behaviors; interpretation of non-verbal behavior; and the therapist's non-verbal behavior.

In attempting to assess the global interpersonal effect of the patient, one might conceptualize his non-verbal behaviors along a dimension relating to the classic Jungian continuum of extraversion-introversion. The therapist might consider the extent to which the patient seems to exert force on his environment by his actions, to what extent does he appear to externalize energy or to what extent does he appear constricted, seeming to avoid exerting force on the environment. Related to this issue of force are the issues of body size and of physical attractiveness. It seems intuitively clear that dealing with persons taller than one's self is different from dealing with those shorter, and that there may be an element of threat involved for patient or for therapist. Those who might doubt this need only to ruminate about treating a six foot five inch 240 pound paranoid as opposed to a five foot five inch 120 pound paranoid. And yet the shorter man may use his physique to create a greater aura of force around him than does the taller man.

If one turns from the consideration of body size and considers the variables introduced by the consideration of attractiveness, the issue becomes infinitely various. Here the global impact of native attractiveness, vitality, grooming, posture, clothing and cosmetics produce effects difficult to formalize but undeniably influential in producing an interpersonal effect. It is crucial to note that this effect is truly interpersonal and does not depend upon the patient alone; a beautiful and vivacious female patient will no doubt exert a somewhat different influence on a male therapist than on a female therapist. Similarly an attractive female therapist will affect a male patient differently than a female patient.

In addition to the gross questions of the amount of force derived from the patient's physical attributes and the typical direction of that force, there is a question of technique of communication. Some persons exert force subtly, others more overtly. All of these factors, and many others such as voice tone, capacity for eye contact, etc., undoubtedly combine to form an overall image of the person, and to affect the behavior of others in relation to him. One communicates and receives many subtle messages on this level; the more of these of which the therapist becomes aware, the more effective and satisfying the therapy should become. It is especially important that the therapist become aware of his own interpersonal effect; while this type of information is difficult to elicit even from one's best friends, it is worth seeking out.

Having briefly reviewed the concept of the global interpersonal effect, we may turn our attention to social role communications. In this category we consider such factors as dress and volitional behaviors. The therapist may consider whether the patient's attire is appropriate for a person of his age, sex, socio-economic status and the occasion at hand. Clothing may be inappropriate in terms of taste, fit or condition. One should particularly note grooming habits and their appropriateness, because these often mirror the course of therapy. A very sick patient may be sloppy, slovenly or bizarre in his choice of clothing or manner of grooming. As improvement takes place he begins to be more conscious of his appearance and the impression it makes on others. Another patient may overdress or be too meticulously groomed at the beginning of treatment, perhaps as an attempt to compensate for feelings of inferiority, or in an attempt to seduce the therapist. As therapy progresses this need should no longer be so evident.

As an example of volitional behaviors which may be considered, the therapist might observe which seat a patient occupies in the office. Of course, if one restricts the patient to the couch or has only one chair for him he has no choice, but if he is free to select one of a group of chairs the selection may be revealing. Although anxiety probably plays a role, the principal determinant of seat selection is likely to be the status of the patient's feelings about the therapist. The patient with more positive feelings may tend to occupy a seat closer to the therapist or one with fewer intervening furnishings. If the chair is relatively light it may be moved frequently during the course of an hour. Sometimes a patient will rise and actually move it a good deal; more frequently movement is accomplished in very small increments. The patient will half-rise in an apparent effort to shift his position and the chair will be propelled forward or backward for perhaps an inch. If and when these or other such voluntary movements occur, they should be noted by the therapist, always with the intent of achieving additional understanding of what is transpiring in his patient and between himself and the patient.

Another very important class of non-verbal events to be considered are apparent attempts by the patient to induce the therapist to take some physical action, frequently an action in which the therapist would serve him in some manner. Presumably this satisfies some need on the part of the patient and may be indicative of the status of his feelings toward the therapist. The patient may behave in a manner which creates a vacuum for the therapist to fill; for example, the patient may take out a cigarette and fumble for a match hoping for the therapist to assist him or he might cry and then hold out his hand for a tissue. Some patients will come into the office and stand in a manner which clearly indicates that the therapist is expected to help them with their coats. On the way out the patient may stand and wait for the door to be opened, sometimes in a position which makes reaching the knob awkward or which will necessitate the making of some "casual" body contact. Awareness of such behaviors and their probable dynamic meaning for the particular patient allows the therapist to make considered judgments as to how they may be most therapeutically received.

More subtle and difficult to develop acute sensitivity to, but perhaps even more revealing than larger behaviors is the patient's use of his skeletal musculature; posture, muscle tone, facial expression and gestures are all continuously employed for emission of non-verbal signals. Is the patient sitting stiffly or is he sprawled all over the chair? Are his hands clenched? Is he sitting forward perhaps as though ready to attack or to flee? Is he frowning or are his facial muscles slack? Careful observations of tonus and posture almost always can provide clear indications of the level of anxiety; posture may also be indicative of the feelings of the patient toward the therapist. The most obvious example of the expression of such feelings is seductive behavior. Manipulating the body in a suggestive manner, movements which drape the clothing in a provocative fashion and other behavior of this type will, however, usually be noted. Other types of feelings may also be expressed. For example, the patient may sit in a posture which conveys insolence or an insulting attitude or may hold himself rigid and erect as if wishing to maintain distance and control of himself.

There are a number of autonomic indices which can be observed in the therapy situation; most of them are associated with anxiety. Tremor, other than that which is indicative of neurologic disorder, can occur with anxiety. Sweating, particularly of the palms and on the face, and dilatation of the pupils may be observed. Depending upon the seating and lighting arrangements, the therapist can often note the pulse in the neck or the temple. Respirations, which are easily observable, tend to become more rapid and irregular with anxiety. Any of these physiological concomitants of anxiety can contribute to the evaluation of the anxiety level, if the therapist has been sufficiently aware of them that he has some feeling for the patient's characteristic rate and type of response.

In considering the variety of behaviors which can be observed, the reader may reach the disquieting conclusion that there are too many things to consider, none of which is easily formalized or crystallized. How can the therapist attend to each of these behaviors in the midst of verbal interaction? The best approach is to limit the number of behaviors being observed. For example, the therapist might decide to spend a period of time observing the posture of a number of patients in a number of different situations. After a time, observing posture becomes second nature and new facets of behavior can be added. One can, for example, deliberately become aware of respiration and study this in a group of patients until it becomes an automatic observation. Most people, patient or otherwise, are stable in their non-verbal behaviors. These behaviors are quite resistant to change even when this is desired. Thus, the therapist has adequate time to become aware of the unique combinations of behavioral expression of his patient. When and if a behavior pattern changes or is replaced by new behavior the new response is more noticeable than the first. For example, the therapist may have observed that a particular patient tends to have slow even respirations or may never have been aware of his respirations. If on one occasion the patient's respirations become rapid and irregular, this would suggest that some change in his affective attitude has occurred.

Once the therapist has developed confidence in his ability to observe a particular behavior it is possible for him to seek the relationship between his observations and the concurrent verbal behavior. There is a two-part question involved in this relationship. First, did the non-verbal behavior occur with or without verbal accompaniment; and second, did the verbal and non-verbal behavior appear to be in accord or in opposition? It is particularly noteworthy if the behavior appears to be in conflict with verbal productions.

Having chosen a single piece of behavior for examination and noted the contexts in which it occurs, the therapist should then endeavor to interpret it, using, in so far as is possible, the four part scheme given for the interpretation of verbal behaviors. While it is frequently true that a single class of meanings appears indicated by the behavior under consideration, it is important that the inquiry not end at this point if it can possibly be extended to other categories.

Once understood, the non-verbal communication can lead to

interpretation, if this seems desirable. That is, one might say, "I wonder if some of this isn't quite frightening to you," without adding, "your palms are sweating." The question of whether to inform the patient of the particular source of the interpretation is a complex one. One of the issues involved concerns whether the patient will respond to the information by assuming that the therapist has "read" him and thus add to his perception of the therapist as an all powerful figure. That is, one issue concerns how magically the therapist wishes to be seen.

The second issue concerns the need to communicate to the patient that he is a whole person; where there is isolation of affect there may be great value in bringing the patient's autonomic responses and other non-verbal behaviors to his attention. The interpretation of non-verbal behavior for the patient involves precisely the same considerations as does interpretation of statements, and therefore will not be discussed further.

The therapist should also be concerned with the study of his own non-verbal productions. There is, unfortunately, no basis for assessing one's non-verbal productions which is analogous to the use of tape recordings; nonetheless the same types of non-verbal behavior which take place in the patient are simultaneously occurring in the therapist and the therapist should endeavor to be at least as aware of himself as he is of his patient. He should first become familiar with his own characteristic modes of expressing anxiety and other feelings; this heightened awareness should lead to self-searching to discover the bases for the expressed feeling in the particular context in which it occurred.

In addition to exploring the same behaviors which we have discussed with reference to the patient, the therapist has the additional opportunity of exploring his own inner sensations, his "visceral reactions" or less elegantly, his "gut feelings." These are the inner feelings of discomfort which occur during a therapy hour and elsewhere, reactions which seem to serve as an indication that there is more occurring in the situation than one is consciously aware of and which leads, hopefully, to a more detailed examination of the gestalt of the situation.

Having become more sensitive to his own non-verbal behavior, the therapist may cultivate a variety of skills in the non-verbal areas. He may encourage or discourage the patient from continuing a particular line of conversation, indicate approval or disapproval or otherwise communicate, to a marked extent employing only non-verbal techniques. It is important to realize that he most probably is doing this whether or not he is aware of it; awareness should lead to more effective and open use of non-verbal communication as a therapeutic tool.

In summary, we would point out that meaningful communication between individuals occurs on a non-verbal level. Because there are so many factors to be considered, we suggest that these be individually studied and added to the therapist's repertoire at a rate that permits effective assimilation. Attention must be directed as diligently to the therapist's behavior as it is to the patient's behavior.

Chapter IX

THE STICKY HOUR

ALTHOUGH A PRECISE definition of the term "sticky hour" is difficult to establish, a therapist will certainly recognize one when he sees it. Basically "sticky hours" are those sessions which produce a feeling of uselessness in the therapist. He feels at sea, confused and unable to help the patient. Therapy hours are repetitive and lead nowhere. The sessions do not flow smoothly, there are awkward pauses. The patient says the same thing over and over again; nothing appears to be happening.

The sticky hour places a burden on the therapist, particularly the inexperienced therapist who often feels that these difficulties are evidence of his personal ineptitude. These feelings lead to further feelings of insecurity and anxiety in the therapist. At this point in addition to an uncomfortable anxious patient we have an uncomfortable and anxious therapist.

When the therapy hour feels difficult, fruitless and uncomfortable for the therapist it will usually feel equally or more unpleasant for the patient. The difficulty often results from the patient's inability to derive sufficient strength and security from the relationship to proceed with the work of therapy. This is not the fault of the therapist in the sense that it results from his inadequacies of technique or humanity since there are many patients who are very difficult to reach and whose capacity for relating is so limited that at any given point of time they may be unreachable. Such patients typically have had many problems in establishing meaningful relationships; frequently the same behavior that has sabotaged other relationships occurs in relation to the therapist. There is also the realistic but infrequently discussed possibility that the difficulty arises from certain aspects of the particular therapist's personality which may create a situation that is unusually difficult for a particular patient.

While the above sources of difficulty undoubtedly pertain to some situations it is essential that the therapist not grasp at these explanations too quickly since neither can lead to increased therapeutic efficacy. The decision that a patient is unreachable or that the particular therapist is unsuitable often is a form of withdrawal. These are decisions which presume that further therapy is useless. Furthermore, these are far from the commonest causes of difficult hours and if thorough exploration of other explanations proves unproductive there is always time to invoke them.

When sticky hours become a continuing problem in therapy, two possibilities should be reviewed immediately. First there is the possibility that the difficulty arises in the patient's personal life as when the patient is currently undergoing a life experience which is emotionally overwhelming or one which requires a choice to be made.

If the therapy feels stuck, the therapist should investigate this possibility through open ended questioning and through an honest discussion with the patient of the fact that they are not progressing. If at this point the patient begins discussing some overwhelming real life difficulty it may be handled in a manner analagous to therapy, but with certain important features kept clearly in mind. When the patient faces an important decision there is a tendency for the therapist to get caught up in the content and to neglect exploration of the other aspects of the patient's behavior. Dynamic, affective and especially transference problems should also be considered. It is possible that the external event is such that a temporary departure from long term goals is indicated. The therapist must be agile and flexible and able to distinguish between the inconsequential and the important issues.

The second possibility to be considered immediately when

seeking an explanation for the sticky hour occurs rather commonly. It embraces those situations where the therapist and the patient have not arrived at either mutually acceptable goals or a plan of procedure. It might be said that in this situation, therapy has not yet really begun. Some of the difficulties attendant here may derive from the expectation, which is common to many patients, that the therapist will be dispensing advice. This expectation is not being met; the patient may be confused and literally not know how to proceed in therapy to achieve his goals. This may be, in a sense, part of his broader problem but may also be the therapist's problem in not providing sufficient orientation. If so, it must be dealt with early so that therapy may proceed. The best treatment for this problem is prophylaxis; the difficulty will not arise as often if there are mutually acceptable goals and careful planning as to how treatment will proceed. However, it is never too late to return and reformulate goals.

If the explanations already advanced do not appear to offer a sufficient basis for the resolution of the difficulty which is producing the sticky hour, it is reasonable to presume that the patient's behavior is a representation in therapy of a specific problem which he experiences in interpersonal relations. In short, the difficulty is symptomatic and is to be understood just as is any other symptomatic behavior.

There appear to be at least three kinds of patient behavior that can produce the "sticky hour feeling" in the therapist. In order of increasing difficulty these are: (1) patients who produce material which sounds therapeutically relevant but who deny interpretations and do not appear to be making progress; (2) aggressive or controlling patients who verbally assault the therapist, turn the hour into a clear power struggle, and frequently demean the therapist in an attempt to control the proceedings; this type of patient is the obverse of the more passive controlling type who, while proclaiming a desire to cooperate prevents movement by inaction, and (3) the ultimate of the passive controlling patient, the silent patient. When a patient resorts to total or nearly total silence during an hour, the difficulties in the relationship are likely to become so acute as to produce extreme feelings of discomfort in the therapist. This is particularly true when the silence is unexplained. If the patient communicates a feeling of depression and inability to talk, the silence may be quite constructive and acceptable; there may be a real feeling of kinship and closeness. The type of silence which we refer to as the sticky type is a silence wherein the patient does not talk and does not offer an explanation for his failing to do so. The therapist is left to wonder why the silence has occurred, whether he has been inept, and what he might do to solve the problem.

The first step that the therapist must take in endeavoring to resolve difficulties arising from behavior that causes sticky hours is that of attempting to understand the purpose and genesis of this behavior. He returns to the dynamic formulation and tries to grasp the meaning of the patient's behavior and the current disturbances which lead him to function in this fashion. If this intellectual task also leads to a further empathic appreciation of the patient's viewpoint, so much the better. The next step is to delineate as precisely as possible the tactics utilized by the patient in his interaction with the therapist and to evaluate possible responses to these.

Let us consider, as an example, some of the thinking which the therapist with an aggressive patient might do in the process of trying to resolve the problems which have led to a series of sticky hours. Questions such as these should be considered: Does he begin his aggression upon entering the office? Are there particular types of material which are likely to arouse aggression? Is his aggression universal, directed to certain classes of persons, or particularly directed toward me? What are my feelings about this patient? What is the most therapeutically useful way of dealing with this aggression? There are, of course, a large variety of possible alternative responses such as anger, counter-aggression, reflection of feelings, interpretation, etc. By responding in different ways on various occasions the therapist may be able to get a clearer understanding of the dynamics of aggression in his patient. It is also important to consider whether the patient is in treatment voluntarily or is under coercion. If the latter is the case, discussion of the coercion, clarifying the point that the therapist is not one of the coercing parties, and offering the patient a real opportunity of choosing whether or not to remain in therapy with the present therapist, should be extremely useful. Finally, it should be recalled that the aggressive patient is sometimes "testing" the therapist by attempting to make the therapist reject him. If this is true, understanding the turmoil of the aggressive beginning can, in itself, be a real therapeutic undertaking.

A good pragmatic way of determining the purpose of aggressive or any other behavior is to note the effect of the behavior on others, particularly the therapist. As a first approximation one may assume that the effect achieved is the one which was desired. Commonly, for example, aggression leads to hostility and counteraggression. This may be the most familiar and therefore the most comfortable behavior to which the patient can relate; it may satisfy his masochistic needs; it may serve to prove again the patient's hypothesis about people; or it may serve a myriad of other dynamic purposes. If the therapist responds to the behavior in the "normal" or expected manner, the neurosis may be reinforced. On the other hand, the particular therapeutic response one chooses may be unfamiliar and therefore threatening to the patient and may lead to an exacerbation of the pathologic behavior and thence to the sticky hour. Simple recognition of the upset which may be produced by failing to respond in accord with the patient's expectations can lead to understanding and a more considered response to the aggression. By this we mean that the therapist might frankly state that he is aware that the upset is produced by the threat of not knowing what to expect of the therapist. One might go on to indicate awareness of the related anxiety, to relate this episode to other dynamic experiences, etc.

A very similar approach may be formulated for the patient who was described as producing therapeutically relevant material but continually denying its implications. Here again the effort should be in the direction of achieving understanding of the dynamic and transference problems involved. Perhaps the patient employs an intellectualizing defense. Perhaps one of his strongest needs is to deny the logic of everything which comes from a person whom he perceives to be in a position of authority. It is usually a waste of time to engage in prolonged polemics with an intellectualizing patient; frequently it is more helpful to respond to the affect. The key to discovering the most therapeutic management is a thorough knowledge of the patient's dynamics.

Silence and the silent patient will be discussed in some detail because the most frustrating moments in psychotherapy, particularly for the beginning therapist, are those spent in total silence with a patient. When a patient actively does something which makes the therapist feel inept or foolish, it is momentarily disconcerting but one can soon accommodate, regain his composure and proceed. By contrast, silence seems to be eternal and becomes most oppressive. Silence is particularly disturbing early in the course of therapy before a relationship evolves. At such a time, the therapist's task is to understand the meaning of the silence and conceptualize how to deal with it, in spite of feeling somewhat awkward and useless.

Although it is of little comfort to the therapist who feels inadequate and pressed to do something in the situation, it is nonetheless true that silence is generally more uncomfortable for the patient than it is for the therapist. There are, however, some patients who are particularly skilled in employing silence as a weapon. This is sometimes the case when the patient has had a good deal of previous experience with therapy and knows that his therapist is inexperienced. However, it is well to realize that the pressures which silence creates in the therapist are also felt by the patient.

Another somewhat comforting thought is the idea that silence in therapy is not necessarily undesirable. This is true even of prolonged silence. For some patients the knowledge that the therapist is willing to sit with him while he does what he wants, without demanding that he satisfy the needs of the therapist, is a novel, communicative and therapeutic experience. An emotional bond of consequence may develop through this shared experience of acceptance.

A very difficult type of silence for most therapists to relate to is that which represents the patient's characteristic mode of interpersonal communication. In brief, the patient is not verbally communicative under almost any circumstances. In this connection it is only fair to point out that psychotherapists, as a class, are quite verbal and tend to be annoyed when they are frustrated in their need to communicate verbally. The extreme example of poor or absent verbal communication is encountered in the catatonic patient; in lesser form it is most often found in the schizoid individual. Children who have developed the expectation of not being accepted or understood may also retreat into uncommunicativeness as a mode of existence. When dealing with chronically uncommunicative patients it is essential to recall what has been said about the discomfort that silence imposes upon the patient. It is generally desirable, particularly with the schizoid patient, to inform him that one knows it is difficult for him to talk, that one will try to understand and will wait until he becomes comfortable enough to communicate more freely.

If the difficulty with silence manifests itself from the very beginning of therapy the whole process of dynamic formulation and setting of goals is rendered difficult or impossible. The therapist is often uncomfortable because of his inability to develop a confident estimate of the magnitude of the patient's disturbance. Although characteristic uncommunicativeness is a common basis of silence in therapy, the therapist must be careful not to conclude that this is the difficulty without adequate evidence, for such a conclusion tends to place the burden of responsibility on the patient and hence relieves the therapist.

Almost all persons have a genuine desire to communicate. With some, particularly the schizoid patients, the lack of communication does not so much represent a neurotic interaction or some form of repression as it does a way of life. They have never had the experience of adequate communication and simply do not know how to proceed. We tend to take the art of conversation somewhat for granted and may find it hard to appreciate its absence. Patients of the schizoid type tend to make very brief verbal statements which are stilted and to which responding seems difficult. To facilitate the establishment of a relationship with such a patient it is often helpful to plan an area of discussion in considerable detail prior to the therapy session. One might select a particular topic that is germane to the therapy. After selecting this topic questions which may be worth exploring are considered and a good deal of the discussion is planned prior to the hour. As an example, one might have a relatively silent patient with whom there has been almost no discussion concerning the patient's relationship with his father. Based upon other material the therapist has come to a tentative conclusion that the father was a rather passive individual. Further exploration of the relationship might serve the dual purposes of helping to understand the patient's problems while also facilitating communication. Some thought will lead to the formulation of many pertinent questions. What does he remember of his father's attitude toward his schoolwork? Did the father participate in his sexual education? Did he and his father engage in hobbies or other activities together? How did the father respond when discipline was required? Did the father appear to have a different attitude toward the other siblings? What sort of things gave his father pleasure? Was his father a religious man? This example points out how one may develop a line of inquiry relating to a central topic. The response to any of these questions is almost certain to open up additional leads which can result in further discussion. It is not hard to imagine how much easier the hour will be when it is begun with a carefully formulated plan of this type. It is very important, however, to avoid being inquisitorial with one's questions. This can be avoided by being explicit about the helping intent of the questions. It would be preferable, for example, to use the form, "It might be helpful if we discuss . . ." rather than, "Tell me about . . ." or "Did you . . ." While following such a line of inquiry it is wise never to interrupt any statement that the patient makes as this will tend to further discourage his productions. Rather the therapist should consciously think of ways to encourage his verbalizations. One should, for example, be particularly alert to any small conversational leads which the patient introduces.

Whatever the dynamics underlying silence, it is not good therapeutic technique for the therapist to blurt out anything that happens to come to mind as a means of terminating a painful silence. In a general sense, the best weapon the therapist has in these situations is time wisely used. However, simple passage of time is not likely to produce a marked change in these behaviors; changes should occur when the therapist is able to deal effectively with his own feelings about the patient and to act in a fashion which does not serve to reinforce and perpetuate the patient's interpersonal techniques. Therefore, he must select his remarks carefully. Certainly the silence gives one plenty of time to consider a variety of factors in constructing a statement. If there is an overwhelming feeling that a reply must be made to something that has been said or done and nothing appropriate comes to mind, a desirable technique is for the therapist to assume responsibility for the silence. This will relieve both parties of the conflicts which the silence imposes, yet allows time to evolve a therapeutic response. This is easily accomplished by a statement such as, "What you just said is important. If you don't mind, I'd like to think about it for a few moments before replying." This will lead to a focussing of attention on the reply to follow, and will heighten its significance for the patient. It is also perfectly acceptable to indicate one's lack of ability to frame a reply. "I'm sorry but I honestly can't think of anything to say at this point."

In summary, the sticky hour is difficult, particularly for the beginner, because it makes him feel inept. It is best handled by a differential diagnosis of the elements which produce it, and a careful consideration of appropriate therapeutic techniques to alleviate it. It is most important that the therapist avoid being panicked into thoughtless or inappropriate statements. When faced with sticky hours it is important to review one's attitude toward the patient, the dynamic formulation and the goals of therapy. A central theme in our formulation is the fact that patients with psychiatric problems often have difficulties in establishing relations of trust. Frequently these difficulties express themselves in a manner which appears to preclude a successful therapy relationship. It is these difficulties which ordinarily lead to the sticky hour and which require extraordinary therapeutic effort to alleviate.

Chapter X

SPECIAL FEATURES OF PSYCHOTHERAPY WITH CHILDREN

THIS CHAPTER, like the chapter on non-verbal communication, is an attempt to deal briefly with a highly complex and little understood area. The purpose will be to sketch out a point of view regarding some of these problems and to discuss the applicability of our approach to the special problems of psychotherapeutic relationships with children.

Psychotherapy with children is, in many respects, even more difficult than therapy with adults, and requires extensive study and considerable supervision to master. At first glance, there is a most compelling reason for stressing work with children. If one assumes that the emotional problems of adults have their basis in the reactions of the child to his surroundings, it appears reasonable to deal with them in childhood, before they become fixed and an elaborate defensive structure has evolved. Logic notwithstanding there are a number of factors which appear to make child therapy so demanding of the therapist that many well trained child therapists gradually drift into seeing adults.

To begin with, the average therapist appears to regard children as immature, dependent, relatively helpless and to be protected. It does not seem fair to put any pressure on the child, but at the same time it appears that it should be quite easy, with one's supposed superiority, to influence the child to do what is wanted of him. When the child doesn't conform, the

If one avoids making these assumptions about the length of treatment and verbal capacity, psychotherapy with children does not differ from that with adults as much as one might suppose. Because of the way a child comes to therapy in the first place, the child's agreement should be secured before treatment is begun. It should be stressed that talking about and working on problems is difficult and that hard work will be expected. When children are faced squarely and honestly with the questions involved and know of the possibility for help, almost all will indicate a desire for help. One should, however, respect the wishes of those who do not. Frequently a child who refused therapy will return later of his own accord, and will begin treatment more enthusiastically for having been allowed to make this decision.

Once a child has made a commitment to therapy, it follows quite naturally that he comes because he wants to achieve certain goals. It should be made quite clear that his goals will be considered. The therapist should then proceed to develop the dynamic formulation and goals of therapy. The course of therapy is usually marked by more verbal activity on the part of the therapist than would be desirable with an adult and by more discussions which are not clearly labelled "therapeutic," if one takes a superficial view. The child may, for example, describe the content of a television program or speak at great length about a baseball game in which he participated. These are clearly his life's functions in the same sense that a job is an adult's function and are to be considered just as meaningful and therapeutically relevant. From this point of view it is much more difficult to separate meaningful from non-meaningful material in treatment with children. It is necessary that the therapist be much more open and imaginative in his interpretations of material with children than with adults. Also, the child is likely to be less linguistically gifted, less self-reflective, and less bound by conventional symbolism than is the adult patient. For these reasons, the therapist must be much more willing to hypothesize and frankly guess at the child's meaning.

If the therapist encounters difficulty in keeping the therapeutic interviews going, he should examine the goals, evaluate their suitability, and look for weaknesses in the dynamic formulation with the suspicion that there are unknown areas that need exploring. A series of questions developed and written outside of the therapy hour may be introduced. It is possible to set the stage for this type of inquiry by saying, "Johnny, I've been thinking over our discussions and have come to realize that there are certain things about you and your mother about which I know nothing. Would it be all right with you if we spend some time talking about this today?"

If it develops that the child is not capable of discussion it is easy to transfer therapy to the playroom. However, transfer to the playroom should be done with specific purposes in mind and specific strategies thought out. It is probably best for a beginner not to make this shift without a full discussion of the case with his supervisor. It is easy to rationalize the decision, and the playroom provides an easy opportunity for the therapist to withdraw both cognitively and emotionally while still going through the motions of conducting therapy. There will inevitably be rough periods in interviews with both adults and children. These should not be seized upon as excuses or reasons to shift to the playroom until the therapist has really exhausted the possibilities in the office. We realize that the position we have taken is not typical and that it may be criticized as appearing to perceive the child as a little adult. Every child is ambivalent about progress toward maturation and capable of regression or, frequently, fixation. We believe, with reasonable and considered exceptions, that the progressive aspects should be encouraged whenever it is possible to do so, and that regression, when encouraged, should have specific aims, such as permitting the child to express aggressive feelings or permitting the child to experience various activities without being punished.

Much of what has been said about psychotherapy, particularly in relation to attitudes, applies equally to play therapy. There are, of course, some very special features. As with psychotherapy, there are a number of schools of thought as to how to manage play therapy; the material we present is biased and does not attempt to do justice to all of the prevailing opinions.

We believe that play therapy is quite valuable, but that it is the most frequently abused procedure in child therapy. Play sessions flow easily. Most children enjoy playing, as do therapists. It is easy to fall into a pattern of play rather than of play therapy, particularly if the child tends to frustrate one's therapeutic intent. The procedure may be rationalized as being an attempt to be permissive, to allow the child to express himself and to form a relationship. All of these are important tasks in therapy but they do not ordinarily constitute the major goals which one is attempting.

Very frequently, the goal of treatment with a child will be declared to be forming a relationship with the child, or permitting the child to experience a good relationship. Implicit in this point of view is the idea that the child will be able to use the person being related to in a fashion which will automatically be helpful to him. This is a tenuous assumption. First of all it relieves the therapist from too much responsibility, it is too pat, too convenient. A second criticizable aspect of this point of view lies in the assumption that the therapist differs from other people only in his willingness to be used by the child in the way the child wants and needs. While it is true that certain children are capable of using this opportunity in an actualizing fashion, others are not. There is no gainsaying the fact that the relationship is crucial to therapy, it may be the *sine qua non* of therapy. It is not in and of itself a sufficient goal for therapy.

It is not unusual for a child who is being seen for the first time, to be taken immediately to a playroom. He is told nothing of the purpose of the therapist or the visits. Perhaps he elects to play checkers. All too commonly the child will enter "therapy" and continue to play checkers for an hour each week for many months. If the therapy is intensive he may play checkers two or three times a week. During this period there will be no discussion as to why the child is coming and no real therapy taking place in the sense that an expert is applying specific skills as opposed to a nice permissive untrained adult spending time with a child. Let us point out that checkers can form a useful therapeutic game. However, a therapist who becomes involved in playing repeated games of checkers with a child in therapy should answer all of the following questions if the game is to be used for maximal therapeutic benefit. Why has this child chosen to play checkers? Is he avoiding verbal discussion of particular areas? Is he too emotionally crippled or insecure to relate in any other way? How do you know? Is he trying to learn the game? Is he trying to defeat the therapist? Is he so masochistically inclined that he is ensuring that he will be endlessly defeated? These questions then lead to a series of questions concerning the interpersonal meaning of the game. Is the game to be approached as a contest or as a mutually shared experience? Should the therapist instruct the patient in how to play the game? What are the transference and countertransference implications of playing checkers with this child? Is someone assuming that the other party is capable of giving him no more of himself? How does the child react to verbal comments about the game? Who chooses to play? When? Why? Who gets the checkers out and who puts them away? Should the therapist give the child a handicap? Should it be done openly or subtly? Does the child want the first move? Does anyone else play checkers with the child? When? Which of the above factors should be discussed with the child? Has the issue of what else could be done been discussed with the child? Does the child understand why he is coming to see the therapist? Has the game been examined from the viewpoint of the dynamic formulation and been interpreted on all four levels? Is the child using this game to control an anxiety-producing situation? Is the therapist? While other questions will suggest themselves to the alert student, an assiduous attempt to answer all of the above questions will increase the probability that the therapy is being therapeutic.

In an effort to avoid the easy slide into non-therapeutic abuses, the playroom situation should be structured at least to the extent of having the child understand that we are seeing him because of certain stated problems and that our efforts are directed toward alleviating these problems. It should be stated that play is employed as a means of helping the patient. After this type of introduction it is best to go through a rather passive period for a space of at least several hours during which an attempt is made to understand the child's "play language," to grasp the nature of the conflicts in which he seems to be involved and to gain some of his confidence. Thereafter one should become increasingly active verbally as play therapy proceeds.

Verbal productions should consist of interpretations or other therapeutic comments of the same type discussed elsewhere. We may encourage a child to involve himself in what we feel is a more therapeutically effective play activity. Very often the child is encouraged to shift gradually from play to talk. We attempt to remain aware of a child's current life functioning and have no reluctance to bring up important issues that arise. If, for example, it appears that a child is about to be dismissed from school, we will actively and directly work on this difficulty. This is done with the belief that the secondary ramifications, such as diminished peer contact and social disgrace will, in themselves, produce further personality problems.

There is one major difficulty in the application of our system of analyzing tape recordings to play therapy. The difficulty arises from the fact that a good deal of play therapy is nonverbal and the verbal behavior which does occur tends to take place over a wider geographic area. These factors make tape recording difficult or inadequate and effective microscopic review of the sessions is hampered, although the therapist can recall a good deal of the hour from notes. It is helpful to have supervisor or peer-group supervision which involves some observation of the play sessions. Play activities are just as classifiable as are verbal statements. For example, a child may paint a picture of a horse. The level of content analysis will see it as just a horse which may be related to a recent experience he had involving horses in one way or another. Inquiry might reveal a television program he had viewed. At the same time the painting of the horse will be expressing feelings. We might conjecture, depending upon our knowledge of the child and the appearance of the painting, that there is a feeling of loneliness or a desire for freedom. Dynamically, the horse might represent a desire to assume a strong masculine role. The transference interpretation could conceivably involve a desire to have the therapist play a role in taming the child or helping him with impulses toward acting out. Viewing all play activities in this frame of reference is helpful.

While our views about the conduct of play therapy are strong and are probably not acceptable in whole or part to therapists of some persuasions, we wish to emphasize our belief that play therapy in merely a specialized technique of psychotherapy. As such it requires the same attention to detail and the same careful planning and review as does any course of psychotherapy. The therapist who views the play hour as an easy hour in his day is, in our opinion, cheating his patient and deluding himself.

We do not mean to present an overall condemnation of play therapy, but rather to make the point that it is not always the treatment of choice. Play therapy is a tremendously difficult enterprise and is one that is frequently totally misused. We feel that a therapist who does not have a reasonable amount of successful experience in the art should not undertake play therapy with a child without prior commitment on the part of an experienced therapist to provide extensive supervision, much of it in observation of the treatment. Without this, much of what passes for play therapy by the inexpert is of little or no therapeutic value, costs time, discourages parents, children and therapists and is ethically questionable, at best.

There are four reasons for taking what may appear to be an extreme skeptical position on play therapy. The first is that it is relatively non-specific, second misused, the third that it may be demeaning to the patient and the fourth that it is too difficult when done properly. Concerning the non-specificity of most play therapy, the following statement can be made. We have seen a considerable number of children at our child guidance clinic and have found that a considerable proportion of them have relatively specific conflicts and interpersonal problems. It has been reasonable and profitable to assume that at least some of these can benefit from the directness and specificity possible in verbal discussions. In many of these cases play therapy would serve only to make it more difficult to help the child.

Concerning the possibly demeaning nature of play therapy, we must remember that frequently our patients have very poor concepts of themselves. If they have the impression that they are being taken to a person who is going to try to help them with a serious problem they have been having, they will build up certain expectations based upon what they are told by their parents and their friends and their previous contact with doctors. If this person then takes the child immediately into a playroom, says, "you may play with anything you want" and then sits passively by watching the child, it is likely to be interpreted as a sign that the person views them as being of little stature. If the child has set up expectancies that he will be helped he is likely to respond to unstructured play therapy with disappointment and rather routine play. Finally, even if the child is helped, there is the danger that he will perceive this help as having come mysteriously from an omniscient adult or a magic playroom rather than having been a product of a reasonable effort of his own. On the other hand, play therapy may offer the tantalizing opportunity of demonstrating to the child that he is understood; understood in his own terms and in his own language. The difference in result is highly specific for the individual. In any case it should always be made clear that the purpose of the play is to help him and to understand him.

Unlike most adult patients, many children in both verbal and play therapy seek to achieve physical contact with the therapist. This will vary from slight, almost accidental touching to actually sitting on the therapist's lap. This is generally permitted although not encouraged. This and other manifestations of dependency in treatment with children pose very complex questions. Dependency of a child in relation to meaningful adults is a normal state and cannot be viewed solely in the traditional transference manner. Frequently, with very disturbed children, the resolution of the dependency is coincidental with actual maturing rather than with a corrective experience. The therapist must be prepared to evaluate the significance of and accept this dependency and to keep it in proper perspective.

In order to emphasize certain of the special features of

psychotherapy with children and to touch upon some points of procedure not previously mentioned, we will discuss the introduction to an initial interview with a child patient in some detail. This example is not in any way meant to serve as a rigid form but rather to demonstrate an approach which has proved fruitful and comfortable for us, and to indicate some of the variables to be considered in planning one's own efforts.

It is our custom not to see the child until after we have talked with his parents. After completing the interview with the parents, we indicate that it is desirable for them to visit with the child for a few minutes. This expresses our concern for the child's welfare, announces again our intention to see him alone and allows the therapist to relax momentarily. The child is then told that it is time for him to be seen; we deliberately do not ask him, since we are not offering him a choice. Once in the office, it is our preference to seat the child in a position which places no furniture between him and oneself. This direct access appears to make emotional contact easier.

It is a mistake to assume that the child understands anything, either about the therapist or the purpose or nature of the visit. We have seen children from relatively sophisticated families who were told this was an examination for camp or that they were being brought to be punished by the doctor or that the therapist is not a doctor in the first place. Our interview, therefore, begins with an explanation of the role of the therapist. This merges into a discussion of problems in general and specific problems which the child is experiencing. An example will demonstrate the dimensions involved in this discussion.

Once settled in the office the therapist might proceed as follows:

"John, when I introduced myself to you before, I said I was Dr. Jones. However, I'm not sure that anyone has told you what kind of doctor I am or why you're here today?" The response to both halves of this question are usually in the negative. Even when the child indicates some knowledge it is usually fragmentary. Because of this, it is our custom to make a fairly prolonged statement at this point. The statement is designed to relieve anxiety, to transmit feelings of respect, to indicate confidentiality and to develop the interview to the point where the child will begin to talk. If this orienting statement is well handled it is not uncommon for a child to interrupt toward the end of it to tell of his problems, albeit briefly. If the child doesn't interrupt, the statement is continued until one has the feeling that the child is ready to talk. One can usually sense when this point has been reached. "John, it certainly seems to me that it would be fair for you to know all about this visit. I know that I wouldn't want to see a doctor without knowing a good deal about him and why I'm going. What I am is a psychiatrist. That's a long word which you may have heard but maybe you are not sure of what it means. I like to think of myself as a 'talking doctor' . . . particularly a talking doctor for children. I see children who have all different kinds of troubles and I try to help with them. I generally don't give shots or pills or take x-rays but try to help by talking. I can't always help, so I can't promise that I can make things better. Part of the reason I can't promise is because it depends on how much you might want to be helped with your problems. I can, however, promise that I will try to be of help.

"That is one of the funny things about my work. I can only be of help if the child will work with me. John, if you decide that you don't want to have anything to do with me and don't want to discuss your problems, I will try to understand how you feel and won't get angry, but, at the same time I won't be able to help you. The other funny thing about my work is that children are my patients, not their parents. I am willing to keep secret anything a child tells me. It would be just between you and me. If I wanted to tell something to your parents I would ask your permission and if you said 'no' I would not tell it even if your mother and father wanted me to.

"John, I'd like to explain something about the kinds of problems children sometimes see me about. Sometimes I see children who have trouble getting along with their mother or father. I talk to children who have trouble getting along with brothers and sisters. Some children have difficulty making friends. Others can't seem to do so well in school. Some children can't seem to keep themselves from stealing. Most of all, though, I see children who are unhappy. I know that unhappiness usually causes the other troubles, so that if we can talk about the things that make someone unhappy we can often help with the troubles. John, I wonder if you could tell me something about the problems that bring you here to see me?"

When presenting the list of problems we attempt to do it dramatically. The list always includes the particular problems that the parents have presented. Frequently the child's face will light up with pleasure when he discerns that you have demonstrated that his problems are acceptable and that you are willing to deal with them without rancor. If he does not bring up problems spontaneously after this preparation we do not attempt to wait until he is very uncomfortable but rather suggest that "I know it's difficult to start talking about problems. Would you prefer to have me ask questions?" With these techniques it is most unusual to find a child who does not respond. One must bear in mind that it is not just the words employed that set the atmosphere of this interaction. Rather it is the therapist's sincerity as conveyed through the words. The child should feel that he is a genuine partner in this enterprise, and that he is capable of relating in this manner.

The remainder of the initial interview proceeds much as with adults except that the therapist may tend to be more active verbally. The therapist may feel free to inquire into any aspect of the child's functioning and do so with the firm expectation that the child will meaningfully review each area with him.

Finally, we turn to the question of the simultaneous treatment of a parent and child. The therapist is usually presented with the child as the problem but this is too superficial a view. There is no question but that if one holds a dynamic orientation toward psychopathology, the inevitable conclusion after seeing a disturbed child is that there is a family disturbance. The logical end point of such a conclusion in many cases might require efforts to treat both parents as well as the child; this theoretically logical conclusion runs into one or both of two frequently insurmountable barriers. The first of these is the availability of therapists. Child guidance centers are generally swamped with work; very few families are equipped financially to provide private care for a number of family members and, even if they are, it is still difficult to make the necessary arrangements. The other relates to the question of motivation on the part of the parent. We believe that good psychotherapy requires a deep desire to change and ordinarily avoid making recommendations which appear destined to fail for lack of sufficient motivation.

Taking all of these factors into consideration we ask the following questions: Who appears to need help the most? Who wants help? Who would most likely respond best? What arrangements can be made for therapists? These questions need to be raised in a cooperative spirit with the family. It is obvious that compromises will often have to be made. Rather than wringing one's hands and bemoaning the awful fate that is likely to befall the child under compromise approaches to therapy, one should remember that we really know very little about what is necessary for satisfactory adjustment and should make the most of what is available.

If one elects to treat only the child, this does not mean that there is never any contact with the parents. There must be periodic brief contacts and an occasional longer contact. Sometimes a regular allocation of five or ten minutes of the hour to the parent proves helpful.

If more than one member of the family is to be treated, the question of whether one therapist should treat more than one of them arises. Simultaneous treatment poses difficulties for the therapist, particularly in trying to preserve confidentiality with each of the persons. At the same time it provides advantages in that the therapist can obtain a broader view of the situation. We do not feel that there is a single solution to these problems; each therapist will have to arrive at a policy which is workable for himself.

As mentioned above, the focus in treating parents who come primarily because of problems with a child ordinarily needs to be somewhat different than if one were treating the parent as an individual desiring therapy in his own right. This derives from the fact that children are growing and may not be able to wait for sufficient change to take place in the parents with ordinary long term treatment approaches. The delay in the aquisition of certain stages of emotional maturity and social skill in itself can become a severe problem and compensating for this may pose great barriers for the child. It is important then, for one to evolve a treatment program for the parent which takes into account the child's need to grow up. The means employed to accomplish this vary. Sometimes a parent's neurosis can be deflected away from the child without really curing the neurosis. On other occasions it will appear appropriate to suggest various means of broadening the child's contacts outside of the immediate home environment. In any case, the presence of the child in treatment will make treatment of parents a different matter than if this were not true.

We have attempted to review briefly the problems associated with treatment of children. We feel that we should end on a note of encouragement. Children can be a joy to treat. Often their naivete enables them to see truths that we tend to conceal from ourselves. Being somewhat incompletely bound by a morass of social custom they may serve as a more honest mirror to ourselves, increasing our knowledge and insight. Further, a young person entering the field might well consider working with children because this is probably the direction of the future. It appears likely that during the next decade or two the focus of the mental health professions will be on early prevention and on the treatment of younger patients.

Chapter XI

ANNOTATED BIBLIOGRAPHY

THIS CHAPTER consists of brief reviews of a number of books which deal with therapeutic interaction. In constructing the list, the goal was to present as diversified a selection as possible, and to include both the standard works and newer works which introduce points of departure in therapy. Our hope is that the student will find among these works one or two books which, for him, serve to provide a basic approach to therapy and perhaps three or four others which provide additional insights and ideas about dealing with patients.

1. Alexander, Franz, and French, Thomas M., with others: *Psychoanalytic Therapy.* New York, Ronald Press, 1946.

This book was one of the earliest publications of what is sometimes called the Chicago school of psychoanalysis. Half the book is given over to a re-evaluation of psychoanalytic technique. The other half discusses case material in light of this re-evaluation. In evaluating psychoanalytic technique the authors discuss the need for flexibility in treatment and the need to view transference problems as they are affected by the behavior of the therapist. A central chapter concerns the definition and discussion of the corrective emotional experience. Although it is not clear that this book represents the current point of view of the authors, it is interesting both as an early example of "neo-Freudianism" and as a collection of ideas about therapy.

Selected reading list
pp 353

2. Colby, Kenneth M.: *A Primer for Psychotherapists.* New York, Ronald Press, 1951.

This slim volume is directed toward moderate goals. The author states that "Like all primers, this is a small book of elementary principles written for beginners." It is probably the best first book for the beginner to read. The author would, however, certainly agree with the necessity of moving on to more detailed works. It is also an interesting book to reread after several years of therapy experience.

No Bibliography
pp 167

3. Ekstein, Rudolf, and Wallerstein, Robert S.: *The Teaching and Learning of Psychotherapy.* New York, Basic Books, Inc., 1958.

The authors present their view of the theory and technique of supervision of psychotherapy students. The parallels of the therapist-patient and the supervisor-therapist relationships are clearly drawn; the dissimilarities in the two kinds of relationships are also delineated. Throughout the book, principles are illustrated through the use of extensive anecdotal material. Although the book is oriented toward the development of supervisory skills, the student will find much which is relevant to the understanding of his current role as student, and much that is stimulating concerning his probable future role as supervisor. From the supervisor's point of view this book contains one of the best possible bibliographies on teaching therapy.

Extensive Bibliograpy on training
pp 334

4. Frank, Jerome D.: *Persuasion and Healing. A Comparative Study of Psychotherapy.* Baltimore, The Johns Hopkins Press, 1961.

This is a volume which deals with the theory of the alteration of behavior through persuasive techniques. The author devotes himself for the most part to the exploration of the common elements in a variety of healing methods ranging from the psychiatrist's couch to the shaman in a primitive society. These are compared and explored for common values. Stylistically this book is simple, candid and highly readable; its effect is that of producing a searching re-examination of one's own beliefs and practices. Perhaps this is the highest tribute that one can pay to an author.

Extensive Bibliography
pp 282

5. Fromm-Reichmann, Frieda: *Principles of Intensive Psychotherapy.* Chicago, University of Chicago Press, 1950.

This book is the summing up and systematization of the therapeutic experiences of a gifted clinician, written with a view to teaching both an approach and a set of principles to the new therapist. The author discusses a variety of technical issues from the point of view of the interpersonal or Sullivanian school of therapy, integrating her arguments with a wealth of case material. The core of the book is a discussion of the therapeutic process, including a chapter on the when and how of interpretation. Throughout, the author's sensitivity to and insistence upon the "here and now" aspects of transference is both enlightening and fascinating. An excellent and important book.

Selected Bibliography
pp 235

6. Garrett, Annette: *Interviewing—Its Principles and Methods.* New York, Family Service Association of America, 1942.

This brief monograph has been a classic in the field of social service for the past two decades. It is lucidly written and easily read. The first half of the book describes various technical aspects of interviewing. Nothing is deemed too "simple" for discussion, making this section of particular value, especially for students who are embarrassed to ask about fundamentals, yet need help with them. The second section contains nine interviews and comments, providing illustrations for the didactic material.

No Bibliography
pp 123

7. Gill, Merton, Newman, Richard, and Redlich, Fredrick C.: *The Initial Interview in Psychiatric Practice.* New York, International Universities Press, 1954.

This volume focuses on the initial interview but provides a variety of material that is quite applicable to psychotherapy generally.

The authors begin with an interesting review of the history of the initial or diagnostic interview. They then present their own approach, which attempts to get away from formal system reviews and mental status examinations in favor of an appraisal of the patient's functioning and reinforcement of his desire for help.

Three interviews are presented verbatim, two with psychoneurotic patients and one with a psychotic patient. The combination of the recording, the transcription and the comments is unique and valuable.

Selected Bibliography
pp 423 and Three 12" L.P. records

8. Grinker, Roy R., *et al.*: *Psychiatric Social Work: A Transactional Case Book.* New York, Basic Books, Inc., 1961.

This book is somewhat strangely titled. It is an attempt to develop a theory of therapy based upon analytic underpinnings but utilizing insights gained by Sullivanians, exponents of communication theory and role theory. In may parts of the book the authors make it clear that they are addressing psychologists and psychiatrists as well as social workers, although one portion of the book is devoted to the particular problems of the intake interview. The crux of this point of view is that one treats patients by modifying their capacities to relate. One does this, at least in part, by being aware of the implicit and explicit roles that are played by the two persons involved. Most of the book is built around a discussion of the treatment of a single case. This is an interesting, although at times quite difficult, book about a relatively new point of view on psychotherapy.

Extensive Bibliography
pp 329

9. Hill, Lewis B.: *Psychotherapeutic Intervention in Schizophrenia.* Chicago, The University of Chicago Press, 1955.

This book is the distillate of a long clinical career. Hill

possessed rare and penetrating insights into people and had the ability to transmit these to the reader with considerable clarity. It is must reading for those who deal with schizophrenics and is most valuable reading for anyone dealing with behavioral problems of any sort. This is the type of book that one returns to periodically, each time acquiring new and valuable ideas.

No Bibliography
pp 216

10. Kelly, George A.: *The Psychology of Personal Constructs.* Volume Two, Clinical Diagnosis and Psychotherapy. New York, W. W. Norton & Company, 1955.

The author presented, in Volume One, his theory of personal constructs based upon the philosophy of constructive alternativism. In this volume he pursues the implications of his theory for psychotherapy. This volume consists of an orderly, detailed and well illustrated discussion of diagnosis and the process of therapy. Included are discussions of specific therapeutic techniques for dealing with a number of problems in the therapeutic interaction. The context of personal construct theory and its systematic vocabulary may present some difficulty, but a summary of the theory and a good glossary are provided. This volume offers much which is both thought provoking and concretely helpful to any but the most ardent advocate of some other theory.

No Bibliography
pp 559 – 1218

11. Menninger, Karl: *The Theory of Psychoanalytic Technique.* New York, Basic Books, Inc., 1958.

This book is Menninger's exploration of the theory underlying classical psychoanalysis. As such, it is not an attempt to teach one to "do" psychoanalytic therapy, rather it is an attempt to understand what goes on between the therapist and the patient in analysis. The author begins by discussing the nature of the contract or agreement between the two persons involved, and then turns to the classic triad of regression, transference and resistance in psychoanalysis. The major usefulness of the book for the non-analyst is to make the goals and techniques of psychoanalysis as a treatment method more comprehensible, and to sharpen one's thinking about the implications of one's own therapeutic technique.

Extensive Bibliography
pp 206

12. Rogers, Carl R.: *Client Centered Therapy.* Boston, Houghton Mifflin Co., 1951.

This is the best single introduction to non-directive or client centered therapy. In it the author discusses his theory of therapy and therapeutic technique, as well as his theory of personality. Although this point of view has been extended and clarified, it has not been altered very much in later works by the author and his followers. Included in the book are chapters about the extension of Rogerian theory to play therapy, group therapy, teaching and administration. This is an interesting book for the non-Rogerian both because of the importance of this point of view among psychologists and because the author challenges many of the assumptions about therapy held by other schools of thought, such as the necessity of establishing a diagnosis and the crucial nature of the transference relationship.

Extensive Bibliography
pp 560

13. Rubenstein, Eli A., and Parloff, Morris B. (Eds.): *Research in Psychotherapy.* Washington, D. C., American Psychological Association, Inc., 1959; Strupp, Hans H. and Luborsky, Lester (Eds.): *Research in Psychotherapy.* Vol. II Washington, D. C., American Psychological Association, Inc., 1962.

These volumes contain the proceedings of two major conferences on psychotherapy research. The earlier was devoted to the broad field of therapy research in an attempt to collate and integrate findings to date; the later conference focused intensively on three areas—the therapist's contribution in the treatment process, the measurement of personality change in psychotherapy and the problems relating to definition, measurement and analysis of significant variables in therapy. Together these volumes are an excellent overview of the present state of scientific knowledge relevant to the art of psychotherapy. As such, they deserve the attention of all who are interested in this field either as practitioners or as researchers.

Extensive Bibliographies for most papers; most citations are to journal articles.
Vol. I, pp 293;
Vol. II, pp 342

14. Ruesch, Jurgen: *Therapeutic Communication.* New York, W. W. Norton & Co., 1961.

This is the fourth in the series of books which Ruesch has written discussing man as the sender and receiver of messages. In this book he focuses upon "the empirical observation of the communicative process" as it is seen in therapy. The book is filled with novel ideas and techniques for listening to what the patient is saying, and for choosing when and how to respond to it. Most impressive is the fact that the author is able to introduce his point of view while remaining in contact with more traditional viewpoints about therapy. A fascinating book which will almost certainly become required reading for psychotherapists.

Extensive Bibliography
pp 468

15. Shands, Harley C.: *Thinking and Psychotherapy: An Inquiry into the Processes of Communication.* Cambridge, Harvard University Press for the Commonwealth Fund, 1960.

The author has endeavored to demonstrate a continuity in theory across the diverse fields of neurophysiology, psychiatry and sociology, employing their common concern with the transmission of coded information as the unifying concept. The psychotherapeutic interaction is discussed in the context of the proposed theory and as a source of validating information relevant to the theory. This presentation is extremely thought-provoking and difficult; it requires a slow contemplative reading but it is well worth the effort.

Extensive Bibliography
selected from diverse fields.
pp 319

16. Sullivan, Harry S.: *The Psychiatric Interview.* New York, W. W. Norton & Company, Inc., 1954.

We are indebted to Sullivan's editors who assembled this material posthumously. It is easily read, easily understood and demonstrates a depth of clinical insight into the interviewing process that is unrivaled by any other publication. Sullivan's observations are penetrating, human and borne out by experience; there are numerous practical suggestions for solving interviewing problems. This book is an absolute must in the preparation of a psychotherapist.

No Bibliography
pp 246

17. Thompson, Clara: *Psychoanalysis, Evolution and Development.* New York, Hermitage House, 1950.

The author reviews the development of psychoanalytic theory from the time of Freud's earliest formulations to the post World War II period. The organization and internal structure of the volume facilitate an understanding of the forces which led to successive revisions of analytic theory by Freud and by those who came to differ sharply with him. The clarity and simplicity with which the author treats many analytic concepts makes this a highly recommended book for the student or other reader who is not very familiar with psychoanalytic theory.

Good Bibliography of analytic writers.
pp 250

18. Witmer, Helen L. (Ed.): *Psychiatric Interviews with Children.* New York, The Commonwealth Fund, 1946.

This volume contains reports of ten courses of psychotherapy with children treated in child guidance clinics by eight therapists representing a variety of theoretical orientations. For each patient the therapist has presented extensive case notes and explanatory comments about his choice of therapeutic actions. This collection offers a rich and enlightening view of child therapy as it is actually practiced on an hour-to-hour basis by expert therapists.

No formal Bibliography, some foot-note citations.
pp 443

19. Wolberg, Lewis R.: *The Technique of Psychotherapy.* New York, Grune & Stratton, 1954.

This volume must be considered the encyclopedia of psychotherapy. While there are certain forms of psychotherapy, notably group therapy, hypnotherapy and other more recent approaches that are not dealt with, the coverage of material dealing with more traditional approaches is extensive. There is, however, a slight bias toward reconstructive or analytic therapy which manifests itself throughout.

The bibliography is a particularly strong feature; there are 481 specific references from the text and five pages of general references arranged by topic. This is not the type of volume that is read from cover to cover, but is more likely to be employed as a reference. It is an important addition to the library of any psychotherapist.

Extensive Bibliography
pp 869

INDEX